POCKET PUZZLES

CROSSWORDS

OVER 130 PUZZLES TO SOLVE

igloobooks

igloobooks

Published in 2019
by Igloo Books Ltd
Cottage Farm
Sywell
NN6 0BJ
www.igloobooks.com

1119 001
2 4 6 8 10 9 7 5 3 1
ISBN 978-1-78905-511-5

Cover designed by Simon Parker
Edited by Bobby Newlyn-Jones

Puzzle compilation, typesetting and design by:
Clarity Media Ltd, http://www.clarity-media.co.uk

Printed and manufactured in China

Contents

CROSSWORD

No. 1

Across

- **1** Hits repeatedly (6)
- **5** Be nosy (3)
- **7** Nationality of Oscar Wilde (5)
- **8** Fifth Greek letter (7)
- **9** Make an earnest appeal (5)
- **10** Living in (8)
- **12** Land surrounded by water (6)
- **14** Quick look (6)
- **17** Ornamental climbing plant (8)
- **18** Gold block (5)
- **20** Shaped like a ring (7)
- **21** More secure (5)
- **22** Eg use a chair (3)
- **23** Important topics for debate (6)

Down

- **2** Weigh down (7)
- **3** Deceiving (8)
- **4** Speech impediment (4)
- **5** Four-wheeled carriage (7)
- **6** Golfing measure of distance (7)
- **7** Senseless (5)
- **11** Component parts (8)
- **12** Sets fire to (7)
- **13** Opposite of shortest (7)
- **15** The weather conditions in an area in general (7)
- **16** Lucid (5)
- **19** Product made from soya beans (4)

CROSSWORD

No. 2

Across

7 Pure (13)
8 Extremely delicate (8)
9 Anxious; nervous (4)
10 Soaked in liquid (7)
12 Cram (5)
14 Type of primula (5)
16 Pulls back from (7)
19 Writing fluids (4)
20 Type of book cover (8)
22 Increase in signal power (13)

Down

1 Intertwined segment of rope (4)
2 Stick to (6)
3 Asserted without proof (7)
4 Answer (5)
5 Document granting invention rights (6)
6 Vindictive (8)
11 Science of classification (8)
13 Patio area (7)
15 Instep (6)
17 Circles a planet (6)
18 Act of stealing (5)
21 Dove sounds (4)

CROSSWORD

No. 3

Across

1 Emissary (8)
5 Princess ___ : Star Wars character (4)
8 Proposal of marriage; bid (5)
9 Zeroes (7)
10 Retains (anag) (7)
12 Written additions (7)
14 Slight earthquakes (7)
16 Print anew (7)
18 Separated; remote (7)
19 ___ Els: golfing star (5)
20 Invalid; void (4)
21 Campaigner (8)

Down

1 Fall vertically (4)
2 Elevated off the ground (6)
3 Horticulturists (9)
4 Treeless Arctic region (6)
6 Gas with formula C2H6 (6)
7 Evaluates the quality of (8)
11 Menaces (9)
12 Strong dislike (8)
13 Christmas decoration (6)
14 Intense fear (6)
15 Thought; supposed (6)
17 Polar ___ : white animal (4)

No. 4

Across

1 Speed contest (4)
3 Word for word (8)
9 Flavouring food with aromatic substances (7)
10 Barack ___ : US President (5)
11 Strengthen; confirm (12)
13 Happens (6)
15 Decide with authority (6)
17 Not staying the same throughout (12)
20 Sets of six balls (cricket) (5)
21 Undoing a knot (7)
22 Type of melon (8)
23 Very long period of time (4)

Down

1 Electrical component (8)
2 Ascend (5)
4 Border (6)
5 Variety of wildlife in an area (12)
6 Kitchen appliance (7)
7 Complain (4)
8 Triumphantly (12)
12 Seven-sided polygon (8)
14 Strongly disapprove of (7)
16 Guarantee (6)
18 Select class (5)
19 Nocturnal insect (4)

CROSSWORD

No. 5

Across

1 Pepper plant (8)
5 At liberty (4)
9 Have faith in (5)
10 State indirectly (5)
11 Written copy (10)
14 Pertaining to vinegar (6)
15 Mistakes in printed matter (6)
17 Having three sides (10)
20 Original (5)
21 Game fish (5)
22 ___ Winton: TV presenter (4)
23 Freshwater crustacean (8)

Down

1 Baby beds (4)
2 Pull a sulky face (4)
3 Unending (12)
4 Imperative (6)
6 Act of retaliation (8)
7 Eg resident of Cairo (8)
8 Inharmoniously (12)
12 ___ down the hatches: prepared for a crisis (8)
13 Relating to the Middle Ages (8)
16 Device for warming the air (6)
18 ___ bear: cartoon character (4)
19 Skin irritation (4)

No. 6

Across

1 Fastened; suspended (4)
3 Distresses (8)
9 Started an essay again (7)
10 Elegance; class (5)
11 Gathering of people (12)
13 Title placed before a name (6)
15 Without ethics (6)
17 Immediately (12)
20 Seemingly (combining form) (5)
21 ___ Bloom: English actor (7)
22 Went along to an event (8)
23 Quantity of paper (4)

Down

1 Printed version of data on a computer (4,4)
2 Certain to end in failure (2-3)
4 Leave the nest (6)
5 Lawfully (12)
6 Loud outcry (7)
7 Perceives (4)
8 Effective working together of parts (12)
12 Recreational area for children (8)
14 Competitor (7)
16 Pay no attention to (6)
18 Flinch away in pain (5)
19 Greenish-blue colour (4)

CROSSWORD

No. 7

Across

7 Hinged case hung from the neck (6)
8 Nitres (anag) (6)
10 Make from raw materials (7)
11 Accustom (5)
12 Consumes food (4)
13 Monastery church (5)
17 Feeling of boredom (5)
18 Greek cheese (4)
22 Relation by marriage (2-3)
23 Children's carers (7)
24 Agricultural implement (6)
25 Hit a snooker ball incorrectly (6)

Down

1 Sailing ship (7)
2 Addresses boldly (7)
3 Happen again (5)
4 Interiors (7)
5 Rise (3,2)
6 Iron alloy (5)
9 Capital of Victoria in Australia (9)
14 Technical knowledge (4-3)
15 Charm; enchant (7)
16 Gnawing animal (7)
19 Opposite of lows (5)
20 ___ Balding: TV presenter (5)
21 Unbuttoned (5)

No. 8

Across

7 Codebreaker (13)
8 Large retail store (8)
9 Home for a bird (4)
10 Nip spot (anag) (7)
12 Grows weary (5)
14 Manipulate dough (5)
16 Nearest (7)
19 Wicked (4)
20 Large snake (8)
22 One who studies people who break the law (13)

Down

1 Percussion instrument (4)
2 Protective kitchen garments (6)
3 Supplement to a will (7)
4 Walk heavily and firmly (5)
5 This Is ___ Tap: film (6)
6 Written communications (8)
11 Creature that eats both meat and plants (8)
13 Obviously (7)
15 Ablaze (6)
17 Boring; hard to digest (6)
18 Tease or pester (5)
21 Office table (4)

CROSSWORD

No. 9

Across

7 Chiefly (6)
8 Current of air (6)
10 River in Africa (7)
11 Sheltered places (5)
12 Prying (4)
13 Slatted wooden box (5)
17 Landowner (in Scotland) (5)
18 Body of a ship (4)
22 Country once ruled by Papa Doc (5)
23 Snobbish (7)
24 Wicked (6)
25 Large artillery gun (6)

Down

1 Incredible (7)
2 Total weight of organisms (7)
3 Worked steadily at (5)
4 Type of rock (7)
5 Furnishings of a room (5)
6 Let (5)
9 Pecking order (9)
14 Large marine flatfish (7)
15 Overly enthusiastic (of speech) (7)
16 Taking part in a game (7)
19 Pursue in order to catch (5)
20 Furnaces (5)
21 Pertaining to the ear (5)

No. 10

Across

1 Sudden large increase (7,4)
9 ___ Newton: English physicist (5)
10 Male aristocrat (3)
11 Lighter (5)
12 Fabric used to make jeans (5)
13 Structured set of information (8)
16 Grow in a vigorous way (8)
18 River cove; bay (5)
21 Lindsay ___ : actress (5)
22 Pot (3)
23 Small drum (5)
24 Property professional (6,5)

Down

2 Usefulness (7)
3 Capital of Kenya (7)
4 Planet (6)
5 Easy to understand (5)
6 Crime of setting something on fire (5)
7 Done efficiently (11)
8 Record players (11)
14 220 yards (7)
15 Become tense (7)
17 Living room (6)
19 Narrow roads (5)
20 Leg bone (5)

CROSSWORD

No. 11

Across

1 Shallow ice-cream dish (5)
4 Confirms a decision; supports (7)
7 Chaplain in the armed services (5)
8 Extension of a debt (8)
9 Muscular tissue (5)
11 Tanks for storing water (8)
15 Wedding (8)
17 Fists (5)
19 Instalments of a TV series (8)
20 Assists in a crime (5)
21 A parent's mother (7)
22 Swallowed liquid (5)

Down

1 Put right (9)
2 Serving no purpose (7)
3 Dressed in a vestment (7)
4 Not noticed (6)
5 By word of mouth (6)
6 Game involving pointed projectiles (5)
10 Bag worn over the shoulder (9)
12 Defeated heavily (7)
13 Volcanic crater (7)
14 Make tidier (6)
16 Domesticated llama (6)
18 Brown earth pigment (5)

No. 12

Across

1 Snake-like fish (4)
3 Hopefulness about the future (8)
9 The North Star (7)
10 Plied (anag) (5)
11 Narrow pieces of land (5)
12 Sincere (7)
13 Six-legged arthropod (6)
15 Water diviner (6)
17 Person moved from danger (7)
18 Capital of Ghana (5)
20 Number after seven (5)
21 Capable of relieving pain (7)
22 Splashing with water (8)
23 ___ Giggs: footballer (4)

Down

1 Ebullience (13)
2 Sweet-scented shrub (5)
4 Sent in the mail (6)
5 Imitator (12)
6 Sickness (7)
7 Largest inland sea (13)
8 Long athletics race (5-7)
14 Walk with difficulty (7)
16 Continue to exist (6)
19 Shyly (5)

CROSSWORD

No. 13

Across

1 Free from contamination (4)
3 Spherical (8)
9 Get too big for something (7)
10 Joins together (5)
11 Overwhelmingly compelling (12)
13 Confine as a prisoner (6)
15 Men's tight fitting hat (6)
17 Action of moving a thing from its position (12)
20 New ___ : Indian capital (5)
21 Varnish (7)
22 Group of spectators (8)
23 Give nourishment to (4)

Down

1 Highly productive (8)
2 Armature of an electric motor (5)
4 Towels (anag) (6)
5 Hostility (12)
6 Fatty substance (7)
7 Expose to danger (4)
8 Dictatorial (12)
12 Dared to suggest (8)
14 Rotated quickly (7)
16 Strong-smelling bulb (6)
18 Display freely (5)
19 Thought (4)

No. 14

Across

1 Stargazers (11)
9 Angry dispute (3-2)
10 Grey-brown colour (3)
11 Metric unit of capacity (5)
12 Stood up (5)
13 Conventional (8)
16 Space rock (8)
18 Hazardous or difficult (5)
21 Henrik ___ : Norwegian author (5)
22 Male person (3)
23 Share (anag) (5)
24 Consequently (11)

Down

2 Written law (7)
3 Ornamental screen (7)
4 Papal representative (6)
5 Faint southern constellation (5)
6 Wireless (5)
7 General guideline (4,2,5)
8 Act of going before in time (11)
14 Meat from a deer (7)
15 Surface layer of earth (7)
17 Holy (6)
19 Type of chemical bond (5)
20 Loutish person (5)

CROSSWORD

No. 15

Across

1 Tunnel under a road for pedestrians (6)
4 Extinguish (a fire) (6)
9 River in South America (7)
10 Alternative form (7)
11 Hot rock (5)
12 Burns the surface of (5)
14 States to be the case (5)
15 Big cat (5)
17 Tiny (5)
18 Kind of whisky (7)
20 Tornado (7)
21 Egg-shaped solids (6)
22 Remained in a certain place (6)

Down

1 Takes by force (6)
2 Taking along (8)
3 Hawaiian greeting (5)
5 Remove clothes (7)
6 Flaring star (4)
7 Interruption or gap (6)
8 Supreme authority (11)
13 The origin of something (8)
14 Flotation device in water (7)
15 Trinidad and ___ : country (6)
16 Composite of different species (6)
17 The body below the ribs and above the hips (5)
19 Unwrap or untie (4)

No. 16

Across

1 Fruit with a distinctive shape (4)
3 Central American monkey (8)
9 Becomes less severe (7)
10 Shoe ties (5)
11 Part of the mind (12)
13 Knocked gently (6)
15 Worldwide (6)
17 Regardless of (12)
20 Mature human (5)
21 Alfresco (7)
22 Campaigner (8)
23 Capital of Norway (4)

Down

1 Organism that exploits another (8)
2 Speak without preparation (2-3)
4 Evaluate (6)
5 A large number (12)
6 Give in to temptation (7)
7 Elephant tooth (4)
8 Incomprehensibly (12)
12 Secondary personality (5,3)
14 Agitate (7)
16 Hoaxes (6)
18 Climbing shrubs (5)
19 Letters and parcels generally (4)

CROSSWORD

No. 17

Across

7 Involving direct confrontation (4-2)
8 Number of Apostles (6)
10 Sleepless (7)
11 Oak tree nut (5)
12 Rank (4)
13 Leers (5)
17 Used up (5)
18 Popular martial art (4)
22 Hank of wool (5)
23 Freedom (7)
24 Consented (6)
25 Complex problem (6)

Down

1 Light periods of rainfall (7)
2 Outer garments (7)
3 Snug and nice to wear (5)
4 Knitted garment (7)
5 Deluge (5)
6 Blood vessels (5)
9 Stylishly (9)
14 Herbert ___ : English philosopher (7)
15 Strong reaction of anger (7)
16 Imitator (7)
19 Academy award (5)
20 Hear a court case anew (5)
21 Dark wood (5)

No. 18

Across

1 Sequence of concentric circles (4)
3 Choosing from various sources (8)
9 Bird of prey (7)
10 ___ John: Rocket Man singer (5)
11 Views; observes (5)
12 Ardent (7)
13 Cease to be valid (6)
15 Small N American lynx (6)
17 Experienced serviceman (7)
18 Rope used to catch cattle (5)
20 Clamorous (5)
21 Exceptional; not usual (7)
22 Parts into which an item is divided (8)
23 Remain (4)

Down

1 Public officials (5,8)
2 Snow home (5)
4 Approval; recognition (6)
5 Coat with a metal (12)
6 Of great size (7)
7 Sweets (13)
8 Short tale told to children (7,5)
14 Placing in position (7)
16 Force fluid into (6)
19 Slumbered (5)

CROSSWORD

No. 19

Across

1 Fish-eating bird of prey (6)
4 Not awake (6)
9 Teller (7)
10 Green gemstone (7)
11 Capital of France (5)
12 Zodiac sign (5)
14 Folded back part of a coat (5)
15 ___ Klum: supermodel (5)
17 Ballroom dance (5)
18 Design style of the 1920s and 1930s (3,4)
20 Joined together (7)
21 Poser; enigma (6)
22 Request made to God (6)

Down

1 Hold a position or job (6)
2 Highly seasoned smoked beef (8)
3 Long poems (5)
5 More than two (7)
6 ___ Fitzgerald: famous jazz singer (4)
7 Groups of lions (6)
8 Extremely steep (11)
13 Individuality (8)
14 Tallier (anag) (7)
15 Warming device (6)
16 Livestock food (6)
17 One who puts in a lot of effort (5)
19 Look after (4)

No. 20

Across

1 Bond movie (2,2)
3 Leonardo ___ : actor (8)
9 Choice cut of beef (7)
10 Flat surface (5)
11 Tall plants of the grass family (5)
12 Instructs (7)
13 Entirely lacking (6)
15 World's largest country (6)
17 Thin paper products used for wiping (7)
18 Follow on (5)
20 Organ situated in the skull (5)
21 Letter (7)
22 Author (8)
23 Small fight (4)

Down

1 Disreputable (13)
2 Health professional (5)
4 Inborn (6)
5 Using letters and numbers (12)
6 Attains (7)
7 Exaggeration (13)
8 Body of voters in a given area (12)
14 Holders of land by feudal tenure (7)
16 Courtroom officials (6)
19 Scheme intended to deceive (3-2)

CROSSWORD

No. 21

Across

7 Spite (13)
8 Pertaining to Spain (8)
9 Pay close attention to (4)
10 Primarily (7)
12 ___ Willis: Unbreakable actor (5)
14 ___ Agassi: former tennis star (5)
16 Freshness (7)
19 La ___ Bonita: Madonna hit (4)
20 Using the minimum necessary (8)
22 Something that cannot be done (13)

Down

1 Indian garment (4)
2 Spot (6)
3 Mechanical keyboard (7)
4 Cage for small pets (5)
5 Heavy metal weight used by a ship (6)
6 Fragrant toiletries (8)
11 Good-looking (8)
13 Enclosed fortification (7)
15 Explanation (6)
17 Pasta strip (6)
18 Stop (5)
21 After the beginning of (4)

CROSSWORD

No. 22

Across

1 Guides a vehicle (6)
5 Commander; chief (3)
7 Propels the body through water (5)
8 African country (7)
9 Cool down (5)
10 Liquid waste discharged into the sea (8)
12 Acquires a new skill (6)
14 Side of an arch (6)
17 Expulsion (8)
18 Toys flown in the wind (5)
20 Laughs unpleasantly (7)
21 Inactive (5)
22 Japanese monetary unit (3)
23 Declines sharply (6)

Down

2 Strong-smelling fungus (7)
3 Saving from danger (8)
4 Silvery-white metallic element (4)
5 Drug that relieves pain (7)
6 Do away with (7)
7 Very holy person (5)
11 Absurd (8)
12 Fortunately (7)
13 Refrain from (7)
15 Tightly framed camera shot (5-2)
16 Discharge (5)
19 Ooze (4)

CROSSWORD

No. 23

Across

1 Soft felt hat (6)
7 People who place bets (8)
8 State of matter (3)
9 Positively charged atomic particle (6)
10 Headland (4)
11 Stomach exercise (3-2)
13 Aseptic (7)
15 Needleworker (7)
17 Small rounded cake (5)
21 Con; swindle (4)
22 Eclipsed (6)
23 Snake-like fish (3)
24 Become chaotic and out of control (8)
25 Animal carapaces (6)

Down

1 Contrapuntal compositions (6)
2 Tyrant (6)
3 Hard chalcedony (5)
4 Useful feature of a place (7)
5 Vivid (of a colour) (8)
6 Push forward (6)
12 Inopportune (8)
14 Excessive bureaucracy (3,4)
16 Trance (anag) (6)
18 Trying experience (6)
19 Rejoices (6)
20 Removes the lid (5)

No. 24

Across

1 Sparkle (11)
9 Collection of maps (5)
10 Cry of disapproval (3)
11 Francis ___ : English statesman (5)
12 Minute pore in a leaf (5)
13 North American diving ducks (8)
16 In a shrewd manner (8)
18 Mexican plant fibre (5)
21 Enter data into a computer (5)
22 Good ___ : nice person (3)
23 Intended (5)
24 Awfully (11)

Down

2 Waterfall (7)
3 Subtleties (7)
4 Away from the coast (6)
5 Misplaces (5)
6 Prohibited by social custom (5)
7 Abashed (11)
8 Everything that orbits the sun (5,6)
14 Martial art (2-5)
15 Useful (7)
17 Highly seasoned type of sausage (6)
19 Sense of seeing (5)
20 West Indian dance (5)

CROSSWORD

No. 25

Across

1 Assurance; composure (6)
4 Move slowly (6)
9 Raging fire (7)
10 African country (7)
11 Ceases (5)
12 Nearby (5)
14 Impertinent; cheeky (5)
15 Staple (5)
17 Perfume smell (5)
18 Guglielmo ___ : radio pioneer (7)
20 ___ Bedingfield: musician (7)
21 Pass (of time) (6)
22 Type of hat (6)

Down

1 Get off (6)
2 Inanimate (8)
3 ___ Piper: variety of potato (5)
5 Irregularity (7)
6 Spread clumsily on a surface (4)
7 Have as a consequence (6)
8 Astonishing (11)
13 Merry-go-round (8)
14 Learning institutions (7)
15 Speak in a confused way (6)
16 Very milky (6)
17 External (5)
19 Ostrichlike bird (4)

No. 26

Across

1 Deceptive manoeuvre (4)
3 White flakes in the hair (8)
9 ___ Monroe: famous actress (7)
10 Japanese dish (5)
11 Machine; automaton (5)
12 Not strict (7)
13 Raise in relief (6)
15 Group of seven (6)
17 Remove (7)
18 Capital of Japan (5)
20 Eg taste or touch (5)
21 Washing sponges (7)
22 Boating (8)
23 Dark blue colour (4)

Down

1 Pitilessly (13)
2 Small woody plant (5)
4 ___ Schwarzenegger: actor (6)
5 Destruction of bacteria (12)
6 Brushed off the face (of hair) (7)
7 Coquettishly (13)
8 First part of the Bible (3,9)
14 Pertaining to plants (7)
16 Taken illegally (6)
19 Australian marsupial (5)

CROSSWORD

No. 27

Across

1 Puzzle (6)
7 One of the Channel Islands (8)
8 Animal lair (3)
9 Alcoholic drink (6)
10 Performs in a play (4)
11 Frighten; warning sound (5)
13 Building (7)
15 Portable enclosure for infants (7)
17 Precipice (5)
21 Curved shape (4)
22 Meal eaten in the fresh air (6)
23 North American nation (abbrev) (3)
24 Forbearance (8)
25 Fish with thick lips (6)

Down

1 A wine shop (6)
2 Sacred phrase (6)
3 Country in NE Africa (5)
4 Relies upon (7)
5 Illegal (8)
6 Manic (6)
12 Occurring regularly (8)
14 Retaining (7)
16 Immature of its kind (of insects) (6)
18 Becomes subject to (6)
19 Rummage (6)
20 Type of small fastener (5)

No. 28

Across

1 Sophie ___ : British model and author (4)
3 Reverie (8)
9 Ramblers (7)
10 Grinding machines (5)
11 Pub (3)
12 Flaring stars (5)
13 Looks slyly (5)
15 Moderate and well-balanced (5)
17 Neatens; crops (5)
18 Rubbish container (3)
19 Strange and mysterious (5)
20 Famous Italian astronomer (7)
21 Hand-woven pictorial design (8)
22 Female sheep (pl) (4)

Down

1 Where the Prime Minister lives (7,6)
2 ___ Mirren: The Queen actress (5)
4 Region of France (6)
5 Clearly evident (12)
6 Make more entertaining (7)
7 Of mixed character (13)
8 Altruism (12)
14 Foot support (7)
16 Larger (6)
18 Local authority rule (2-3)

CROSSWORD

No. 29

Across

1 Wish for (6)
4 Threw with force (6)
9 Fry until crisp (7)
10 Lattice (7)
11 Lead a discussion (5)
12 Faithful (5)
14 Muscular (5)
15 Jewelled headdress (5)
17 Stringed instrument (5)
18 Atomic particle (7)
20 Cut of beef (7)
21 Control; regulate (6)
22 In slow tempo (of music) (6)

Down

1 Imperfection (6)
2 Formerly Ceylon (3,5)
3 Sharp blade (5)
5 Totally (7)
6 Quieten down; send to sleep (4)
7 Type of engine (6)
8 Official agreements (11)
13 Submissive (8)
14 Excluding (7)
15 Bicycle for two people (6)
16 Lively Spanish dance (6)
17 God of love (5)
19 On top of (4)

No. 30

Across

1 Suggested or implied idea (11)
9 Faint bird cry (5)
10 Ten (anag) (3)
11 Rinse out with water (5)
12 Nick ___ : politician (5)
13 Cave in (8)
16 Traveller (8)
18 Between eighth and tenth (5)
21 Wound from a wasp (5)
22 Fishing pole (3)
23 Service colour of the army (5)
24 Poorly behaved; impolite (3-8)

Down

2 Small bone (7)
3 ___ power: energy source (7)
4 Long essay or dissertation (6)
5 Theme for a discussion (5)
6 Unit of weight (5)
7 Region including Cornwall and Devon (4,7)
8 Fear in front of an audience (5,6)
14 Illegally in advance of the ball in football (7)
15 Written language for blind people (7)
17 Reach (6)
19 Rafael ___ : Spanish tennis star (5)
20 Nonsense (5)

CROSSWORD

No. 31

Across

1 Shameful (11)
9 Move back and forth (5)
10 Trouble in mind or body (3)
11 Slender woman or girl (5)
12 Mournful poem (5)
13 How a crab moves (8)
16 Cabbage salad (8)
18 Bunches (5)
21 A thing that measures (5)
22 Large beer cask (3)
23 Subside (5)
24 Coordinate (11)

Down

2 Burst inwards (7)
3 Large bird of prey (7)
4 Eagerly (6)
5 Golden ___ : bird of prey (5)
6 Customary practice (5)
7 Revive (11)
8 Double entendre (4,2,5)
14 Johannes ___ : Dutch painter (7)
15 Snobbish (7)
17 Church instruments (6)
19 More delicate (5)
20 Swill about (5)

No. 32

Across

1 Person who copies out documents (6)
5 Tool for making holes in leather (3)
7 Prevent (5)
8 Sculptures (7)
9 Express one's opinion (5)
10 Having a sweet nature (8)
12 Having pimples (6)
14 Breakfast food (6)
17 Someone with the same moniker (8)
18 Long-___ owl: bird (5)
20 Urgent (7)
21 Crisp; pleasantly cold (5)
22 Boy (3)
23 Course of a meal (6)

Down

2 Get up to speed (5,2)
3 Bunches of flowers (8)
4 Disorder; confused situation (4)
5 Person on the staff of an ambassador (7)
6 Given generously (7)
7 Savoury jelly (5)
11 Act of removal (8)
12 Country in Africa (7)
13 Quantity on which a maths operation is performed (7)
15 Sideways; squinting (7)
16 Friendly (5)
19 Swindle (4)

CROSSWORD

No. 33

Across

1 Bear witness (6)
7 Fretting (8)
8 Use a chair (3)
9 Root vegetable (6)
10 Sculpture of the upper body (4)
11 Amorphous shapes (5)
13 Performing a task again (7)
15 ___ harp: instrument played by the wind (7)
17 Lion who rules over Narnia (5)
21 Engrave; carve (4)
22 Part of the eye (6)
23 Rocky peak (3)
24 Hot pepper (8)
25 Entirely (6)

Down

1 Soak up (6)
2 Stain skin with indelible colour (6)
3 Two children born at the same time (5)
4 Held tightly (7)
5 Raise one's ___ : show surprise (8)
6 Agreement or concord (6)
12 Partition inside a ship (8)
14 Transported by hand (7)
16 Background actors (6)
18 Hate (6)
19 Close at hand (6)
20 Device used to sharpen razors (5)

No. 34

Across

1 State of mental strain; anxiety (6)
5 The sound of a dove (3)
7 Inert (anag) (5)
8 Separates into parts (7)
9 Wanderer (5)
10 Excessively emotional (6,2)
12 Functional (6)
14 Throngs (6)
17 Private detective (8)
18 Test or examine a metal (5)
20 Rule of personal conduct (7)
21 Ellipses (5)
22 Coniferous tree (3)
23 Not arranged neatly (6)

Down

2 Suit makers (7)
3 Abruptly (8)
4 Amaze (4)
5 Confined to a small space (7)
6 Exceeds; surpasses (7)
7 Important question (5)
11 Number of days in a fortnight (8)
12 Sad (7)
13 Farnborough ___ : famous flying display (7)
15 Broke free from confinement (7)
16 Hits with a lash (5)
19 Chinese monetary unit (4)

CROSSWORD

No. 35

Across

1 Fictional ugly creatures (8)
5 Bite or nibble at (4)
8 Indian lute (5)
9 Rod used in weightlifting (7)
10 Become less intense (4,3)
12 Fighter (7)
14 Small explosive bomb (7)
16 Covered in stiff hairs (7)
18 Gets away (7)
19 Verse form (5)
20 Part of an egg (4)
21 Person sent on a special mission (8)

Down

1 Young female (4)
2 Foolish person (6)
3 Tempestuous (9)
4 Thief (6)
6 Liam ___ : Irish actor (6)
7 Raging conflagration (8)
11 Extends one's body (9)
12 Swollen with fat (8)
13 Involving financial matters (6)
14 Mineral used to make plaster of Paris (6)
15 Continent (6)
17 Extreme anger (4)

No. 36

Across

7 Big cat (6)
8 Flat; two-dimensional (6)
9 Fine powder (4)
10 Act of treachery (8)
11 Plans (7)
13 During (5)
15 Nasal passageway (5)
16 Govern badly (7)
18 Jovial (8)
19 ___ vera: plant (4)
21 A size of book page (6)
22 Posted (6)

Down

1 Capital of Azerbaijan (4)
2 Reach the required standard (3,3,7)
3 Searched clumsily (7)
4 Malice (5)
5 Miscellaneous equipment (13)
6 Similarity (8)
12 Detailed analysis (8)
14 Certificate (7)
17 Currently in progress (5)
20 Kitchen appliance (4)

CROSSWORD

No. 37

Across

7 Edge (6)
8 Ticket (6)
9 ___ Moore: Hollywood actress (4)
10 Country in Central Asia (8)
11 Triangle with three unequal sides (7)
13 Meadow ___ : songbird (5)
15 ___ White: snooker player (5)
16 Luggage (7)
18 Stated clearly (8)
19 Tuna (anag) (4)
21 Not sensible (6)
22 Detach; unfasten (6)

Down

1 Woody plant (4)
2 Not living up to expectations (13)
3 Stir up trouble (7)
4 Portion of a play (5)
5 Account of one's own life (13)
6 Observing (8)
12 Excerpt from a newspaper (8)
14 Element needed by the body (7)
17 Later (5)
20 Cranny (4)

No. 38

Across

1 The reproduction of sound (5)
4 Provoked or teased (7)
7 Dole out (5)
8 Socialist part of a political party (4,4)
9 Pantomime ___ : comic characters (5)
11 Read out loud (8)
15 End of a railway route (8)
17 Modifies (5)
19 Keep at a distance (8)
20 Woman's dress (5)
21 Variant of a thing (7)
22 Church council (5)

Down

1 Large mass of sliding snow (9)
2 Varies (7)
3 Last longer than (of clothes) (7)
4 Subtle variation (6)
5 US monetary unit (6)
6 Crumble (5)
10 Protected from bad weather (9)
12 Female ruler (7)
13 Unfamiliar (7)
14 Adheres to; fastens (6)
16 Banner or flag (6)
18 Mournful song (5)

CROSSWORD

No. 39

Across

1 Vitreous (6)
5 Seventh Greek letter (3)
7 Lives (anag) (5)
8 Schedule of activities (7)
9 Armistice (5)
10 Yellowish edible seed (8)
12 Mistakes (6)
14 Positive and happy (6)
17 Relating to the heart (8)
18 Very skilled at something (5)
20 In a friendly manner (7)
21 Maw (5)
22 Absolutely (3)
23 Sheepskin (6)

Down

2 Cross-bred dog (7)
3 Footballers whose role is to score (8)
4 Strain (4)
5 Title appended to a man's name (7)
6 Non-believer in God (7)
7 Implant (5)
11 Cooking measure (8)
12 To the same degree (7)
13 Restores honour (7)
15 Modern type of paint (7)
16 ___ Jones: American singer-songwriter (5)
19 Guided journey (4)

No. 40

Across

1 Unable to hear (4)
3 Making law (8)
9 Glisten (7)
10 Shoot with great precision (5)
11 Tree (3)
12 Lubricated (5)
13 Repeat something once more (5)
15 Drive forward (5)
17 Free from dirt (5)
18 Pouch; enclosed space (3)
19 Criminal (5)
20 Makes a journey (7)
21 Clemency (8)
22 Related by blood (4)

Down

1 Rude and discourteous (13)
2 Self-evident truth (5)
4 Scandinavian (6)
5 Worldly (12)
6 Frozen water spears (7)
7 British actress who became an MP (6,7)
8 Impudence (12)
14 Devise beforehand (7)
16 Written in verse (6)
18 Small spot (5)

CROSSWORD

No. 41

Across

1 Enter unlawfully (8)
5 One of the continents (4)
8 Climb onto (5)
9 Summary of events (5-2)
10 Clinging shellfish (7)
12 Armoury (7)
14 Disturb (7)
16 Trialled or tested (7)
18 Pursuer (anag) (7)
19 Vapour bath (5)
20 Sci-fi film with Jeff Bridges (4)
21 Amaze (8)

Down

1 Tone down (4)
2 Escapes from (6)
3 Fatherhood (9)
4 Walk casually (6)
6 Make unhappy (6)
7 Of striking appropriateness (8)
11 Public declaration of policy (9)
12 Artificial water channel (8)
13 Not genuine (6)
14 Loves dearly (6)
15 Long-legged rodent (6)
17 Cloth worn around the waist (4)

No. 42

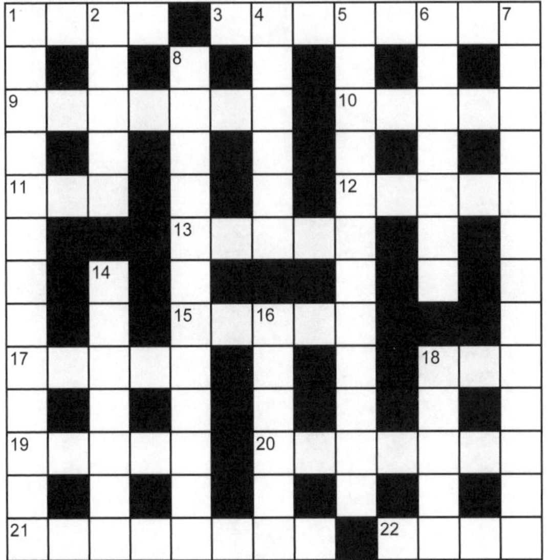

Across

1 Free from doubt (4)
3 Marriage ceremony (8)
9 Sweetened citrus beverage (7)
10 Nasal manner of pronunciation (5)
11 Slip up (3)
12 Taut (5)
13 Enrol (anag) (5)
15 Small marine fish (5)
17 Hat edges (5)
18 Lively dance (3)
19 Feudal vassal (5)
20 Workshop or studio (7)
21 Passing (of time) (8)
22 Main acting part (4)

Down

1 25th anniversary celebration (6,7)
2 ___ Willis: daughter of Demi Moore (5)
4 Country in N Europe (6)
5 Fully extended (12)
6 Spot of bright colour (7)
7 Prone to steal (5-8)
8 Failure to act with prudence (12)
14 Grotesque monster (7)
16 Keep hold of (6)
18 Liquid part of fruits (5)

CROSSWORD

No. 43

Across

1 Soundless (6)
4 Put on a play (6)
9 Pasta dish (7)
10 French city (7)
11 Town ___ : official who makes public announcements (5)
12 Small valley (5)
14 Eg Wordsworth and Keats (5)
15 Aromatic herb (5)
17 Royal (5)
18 Squeeze into a compact mass (7)
20 Blissful state (7)
21 Dough used for pies (6)
22 Stableman (6)

Down

1 Sandstone constituent (6)
2 Pleasingly rich (8)
3 African country whose capital is Niamey (5)
5 Information (7)
6 A parent's mother (4)
7 Of delicate beauty (6)
8 One in charge of a school (4,7)
13 A time-consuming flight (4,4)
14 Pillage (7)
15 Chess piece (6)
16 Participant in a game (6)
17 Takes a break (5)
19 Applies friction to (4)

No. 44

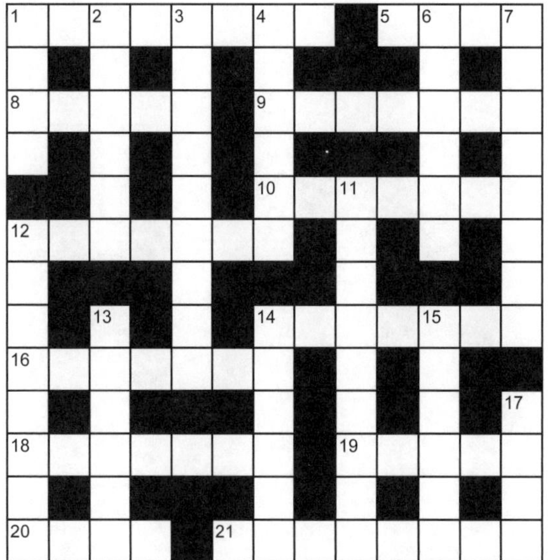

Across

1 Physically strong and active (8)
5 Fit of petty annoyance (4)
8 Rotates (5)
9 Hot wind blowing from North Africa (7)
10 Closest (7)
12 Visible horizon (7)
14 Very low temperature fridge (7)
16 Sharp tooth (7)
18 Coarsen (7)
19 Stroll (5)
20 Animate existence (4)
21 Always in a similar role (of an actor) (8)

Down

1 Poker stake (4)
2 Barely (6)
3 Cherishes as sacred (9)
4 Crazy (6)
6 Male relatives (6)
7 Boundary (8)
11 Weaken or reduce in force (9)
12 Bushy-tailed rodent (8)
13 The back of the neck (6)
14 Period of wild behaviour (6)
15 Country in central Africa (6)
17 Tidy (4)

CROSSWORD

No. 45

Across

1 Gangs (4)
3 Buffers (8)
9 Admirers (7)
10 Golf shots (5)
11 Small shelter (3)
12 Gain new knowledge (5)
13 Corpulent (5)
15 Earnings (5)
17 Form of oxygen (5)
18 Large salt water body (3)
19 Magical incantation (5)
20 London district (4,3)
21 Young (8)
22 Open tart (4)

Down

1 Naughtily (13)
2 Constructed (5)
4 Uncertain (6)
5 Total despair (12)
6 Social reject (7)
7 Thelma & Louise actress (5,8)
8 A grouping of states (12)
14 Henry David ___ : US author and poet (7)
16 Rich cake (6)
18 One of the senses (5)

No. 46

Across

1 Sweet on a stick (8)
5 Insect larva (4)
9 Perspire (5)
10 Fishing net (5)
11 Assertion made without proof (10)
14 Allow (6)
15 Concurs (6)
17 Unbroken existence over time (10)
20 Gold ___ : award for coming first (5)
21 Nursemaid (5)
22 Kate ___ : British singer (4)
23 Senseless (8)

Down

1 In case (4)
2 Look slyly or unpleasantly (4)
3 Understandably (12)
4 Snow leopards (6)
6 Appreciates (8)
7 Lack of hair (8)
8 Uncurled (12)
12 Sample for medical testing (8)
13 Explosive shells (8)
16 Central parts of cells (6)
18 A single time (4)
19 Fitness centres (4)

CROSSWORD

No. 47

Across

1 Opposite of floors (8)
5 Increases; sums up (4)
8 Upright (5)
9 Portable lamp (7)
10 Compels to do something (7)
12 Type of computer (7)
14 Move like a snake (7)
16 Adult (5-2)
18 Character in Hamlet (7)
19 Astonish (5)
20 Feudal labourer (4)
21 Reproduce recorded sound (4,4)

Down

1 US pop star (4)
2 Standards to be aimed at (6)
3 Purpose (9)
4 Ride a horse at pace (6)
6 Remove silt from a river (6)
7 Ominous (8)
11 Roman foot soldier (9)
12 Coerces into doing something (8)
13 Burrowing rodent (6)
14 Spread out awkwardly (6)
15 Capital of Cuba (6)
17 Abrupt movement (4)

No. 48

Across

1 Loathe (5)
4 Before or by now (7)
7 Married man (informal) (5)
8 Fairness (8)
9 Thick; heavy (5)
11 Common salad dressing (5,3)
15 Consist of (8)
17 Waterway (5)
19 Small baked products (8)
20 Call forth or cause (5)
21 Return to a former state (7)
22 Concur (5)

Down

1 Occurring without oxygen (9)
2 Nonconformist (7)
3 More circular (7)
4 Andre ___: former US tennis player (6)
5 Discharges (6)
6 Moneys owed (5)
10 Over the top (9)
12 Coloured bands of light (7)
13 One who finds water by dowsing (7)
14 Less strong (6)
16 Repulsive (6)
18 Variety show (5)

CROSSWORD

No. 49

Across

- **1** Express discontent over (6)
- **5** Extremity (3)
- **7** Removes water from a boat (5)
- **8** Go before (7)
- **9** ___ Robson: British tennis player (5)
- **10** Burning (8)
- **12** Stops (6)
- **14** Entreated; beseeched (6)
- **17** Upsets; agitates (8)
- **18** Dry biscuits used as baby food (5)
- **20** Capital of Thailand (7)
- **21** Beasts of burden (5)
- **22** Organ of sight (3)
- **23** Narrate a story once again (6)

Down

- **2** Aural pain (7)
- **3** City in NE Scotland (8)
- **4** Aromatic herb (4)
- **5** Tidal mouth of a river (7)
- **6** Eg shrimp or crab (7)
- **7** Existing (5)
- **11** Make-believe (8)
- **12** Stately hymn tune (7)
- **13** Absolutely incredible (7)
- **15** Involve in conflict (7)
- **16** Eg arms and legs (5)
- **19** Vend (4)

No. 50

Across

1 Court enclosure (4)
3 Clock timing device (8)
9 Laid open to view (7)
10 Advised; encouraged (5)
11 Very sad (12)
13 Uncover (6)
15 Worshipper (6)
17 Vehemently (12)
20 In a ___ : very quickly (5)
21 Lift up (7)
22 Final (8)
23 Requests (4)

Down

1 Terrible (8)
2 Sleeveless cloaks (5)
4 First born (6)
5 Type of bus (6-6)
6 Less heavy (7)
7 Method; fashion (4)
8 Amazement (12)
12 Dullness of colour (8)
14 Bloodsucking creature (7)
16 Greek goddess of wisdom (6)
18 Jumps (5)
19 Inflammation of an eyelid (4)

CROSSWORD

No. 51

Across

1 Speaks very quietly (8)
5 Chances of winning (4)
9 A hidden storage space (5)
10 Golf clubs (5)
11 Extraordinary (10)
14 Expressing regret (6)
15 Fashions (6)
17 Awkwardness (of movement) (10)
20 Believer in a supreme being (5)
21 Water and rubber mix (5)
22 Unpleasantly moist (4)
23 Unsteady (8)

Down

1 Part of a candle (4)
2 Paul ___ : former England football captain (4)
3 Precondition (12)
4 Nasal (6)
6 Push button outside a house (8)
7 Anxious uncertainty (8)
8 As quickly as possible (7-5)
12 Went before (8)
13 False impression (8)
16 Not level (6)
18 Remnant (4)
19 Shaft on which a wheel rotates (4)

No. 52

Across

1 Expressions (6)
4 Fruit drinks (6)
9 Kneecap (7)
10 Observes (7)
11 Giggle (5)
12 Cuban folk dance (5)
14 Not suitable (5)
15 Wading bird (5)
17 Helmet part for protecting the face (5)
18 Modern; up to date (7)
20 European deer (7)
21 Insect that transmits sleeping sickness (6)
22 Allocate (6)

Down

1 African antelope (6)
2 An unwelcome person; invader (8)
3 Mixture that insulates soil (5)
5 Pompous person (7)
6 Stylish (4)
7 Quick sleep (6)
8 Fabricate (11)
13 US state (8)
14 Alphabetical lists (in books) (7)
15 Not disposed to cheat (6)
16 Mythical sea monster (6)
17 Swerves off course (5)
19 Motivate; desire to act (4)

CROSSWORD

No. 53

Across

1 Walked at a steady speed (5)
4 Give up or surrender something (3,4)
7 Character in Oliver Twist (5)
8 The decade from 1990 - 1999 (8)
9 Religious groups (5)
11 Wrapper for a letter (8)
15 Representations or descriptions of data (8)
17 Mountain cry (5)
19 Assimilate again (8)
20 Stringed instrument (5)
21 Unintelligent (7)
22 Antelope (5)

Down

1 Tepid only (anag) (9)
2 Plot (7)
3 Easily drawn out into a wire (7)
4 Batting order in a cricket team (4-2)
5 Crown (6)
6 Card game (5)
10 Garbled (9)
12 Green vegetation (7)
13 Balearic Island (7)
14 Capital of Germany (6)
16 Break apart (6)
18 Leaves out (5)

CROSSWORD

No. 54

Across

1 Spiny cactus fruit (7,4)
9 Make good on a debt (5)
10 ___ Titmuss: TV personality (3)
11 Yearned for (5)
12 Set of moral principles (5)
13 War memorial (8)
16 Person you work for (8)
18 Timber framework (5)
21 Unspecified object (5)
22 Not on (3)
23 Foolishly credulous (5)
24 Energetically or vigorously (11)

Down

2 Precipitating (7)
3 Heart-shaped (7)
4 Portable computer (6)
5 Recipient of money (5)
6 Embarrass (5)
7 Belief something will happen (11)
8 Deterred (11)
14 Flat highland (7)
15 Believing the worst (7)
17 One's environment (6)
19 Not in good physical condition (5)
20 From that time (5)

CROSSWORD

No. 55

Across

1 Device used to connect to the internet (5)
4 Constantly present (7)
7 Doctrine; system of beliefs (5)
8 Took in (8)
9 Flatten on impact (5)
11 Bouquets (8)
15 Dead end (3-2-3)
17 Precious gem (5)
19 Relating to office work (8)
20 Posed a question (5)
21 Degree of eminence (7)
22 Gold coin (5)

Down

1 Malevolent (9)
2 Repulsion (7)
3 Communication; note (7)
4 Restaurant (6)
5 Continent (6)
6 Asian country (5)
10 Belligerent (9)
12 Beautified (7)
13 Able to read minds (7)
14 Bewail (6)
16 Different from (6)
18 Start of (5)

No. 56

Across

1 Leg bone (6)
4 Diminished (6)
9 Force of civilians trained as soldiers (7)
10 Having few storeys (of a building) (3-4)
11 Manner of speaking (5)
12 Correct (5)
14 Embed; type of filling (5)
15 Scowl (5)
17 Adult insect (5)
18 Japanese army officer (7)
20 Doing as one is told (7)
21 Regardless (6)
22 Signal (anag) (6)

Down

1 Be extremely hungry (6)
2 Extravagant fuss (8)
3 Espresso coffee and steamed milk (5)
5 Establishment for making beer (7)
6 Hired form of transport (4)
7 Opposite of a victory (6)
8 Computation (11)
13 Shining (8)
14 Reluctance to change (7)
15 Dashboard of a motor vehicle (6)
16 Small drums (6)
17 Model; perfect (5)
19 Numerous (4)

CROSSWORD

No. 57

Across

1 Team (4)
3 Inconceivably large (8)
9 Drop (7)
10 Island in the Bay of Naples (5)
11 Tiles (anag) (5)
12 Used for the storage of fat (of tissue) (7)
13 Innate (6)
15 Having been defeated (6)
17 Plants that live a year or less (7)
18 Curt (5)
20 Colour lightly (5)
21 People who make money (7)
22 Longing (8)
23 Legume (4)

Down

1 Remarkably (13)
2 Waggish (5)
4 Stadiums (6)
5 Practice of designing buildings (12)
6 Highest (7)
7 British comedy author (5,8)
8 Underground (12)
14 A rich mine; big prize (7)
16 Towards the rear (6)
19 Pass a rope through (5)

No. 58

Across

1 A large spar (8)
5 Potato (informal) (4)
9 Imitative of the past (5)
10 Not tight (5)
11 The meaning of a word (10)
14 Desire for water (6)
15 Responds to (6)
17 Giving good value for money (10)
20 Variety of coffee (5)
21 Prologue (abbrev) (5)
22 Repeat an action (4)
23 Trapped in a small space (8)

Down

1 Pub rooms selling alcohol (4)
2 Makes damp (4)
3 Opposite of amateur (12)
4 Symbolic (6)
6 Administrative division (8)
7 Profundity (8)
8 Repetition of the same sound (12)
12 Pennant (8)
13 Separated (8)
16 Fierce woman (6)
18 Heavenly body (4)
19 Covering for the head (4)

CROSSWORD

No. 59

Across

1 Tumultuous (11)
9 Old silver coin (5)
10 Untruth (3)
11 Sound of any kind (5)
12 Excess (5)
13 Anxiousness (8)
16 Light brown cane sugar (8)
18 Relating to country life (5)
21 Musical speeds (5)
22 Much ___ About Nothing: play (3)
23 Excuse or pretext (5)
24 Calamity or great loss (11)

Down

2 Final parts of stories (7)
3 Birds of the family Columbidae (7)
4 Competitive games (6)
5 Undo (5)
6 Not illuminated (5)
7 ___ man: type of biscuit (11)
8 Reduction in worth (11)
14 Fear of heights (7)
15 Large extinct elephant (7)
17 Enrol in the armed services (6)
19 Spanish wine (5)
20 South American animal (5)

No. 60

Across

1 Held out against (8)
5 Coalition of countries (4)
8 Stratum (5)
9 Average (7)
10 Hassles; prickles (7)
12 Pledged to marry (7)
14 Template (7)
16 Group of four (7)
18 Unpredictable (7)
19 Towering (5)
20 Clean up (4)
21 Interpret in a certain way (8)

Down

1 Move by rotating (4)
2 Observing furtively (6)
3 Oddest (9)
4 Lengthen (6)
6 Residents of an area (6)
7 Gigantic (8)
11 Groups of musicians (9)
12 Fluent in the use of language (8)
13 Jolted (6)
14 Plaster for coating walls (6)
15 Bestow (6)
17 Sort; variety (4)

CROSSWORD

No. 61

Across

- **7** Cared for (6)
- **8** Eg monkey or whale (6)
- **10** Japanese art of paper folding (7)
- **11** Jessica ___-Hill : British heptathlete (5)
- **12** Repetition of a sound (4)
- **13** Lady (5)
- **17** Relating to birth (5)
- **18** Average value (4)
- **22** Moth-___ : damaged (5)
- **23** Period of violent behaviour by a group of people (7)
- **24** Fatty matter (6)
- **25** Support; help (6)

Down

- **1** Chanted (7)
- **2** Cargo (7)
- **3** Cared (anag) (5)
- **4** Photographic devices (7)
- **5** Alter (5)
- **6** Dental care item (5)
- **9** Huge extinct animals (9)
- **14** Sully (7)
- **15** An edible jelly (7)
- **16** Friendly understanding (7)
- **19** Join together (5)
- **20** Sharply inclined (5)
- **21** Wrong (5)

No. 62

Across

1 Hair colourants (4)
3 Refined and elegant (8)
9 Beginning to exist (7)
10 Boldness; courage (5)
11 Agreed upon by several parties (12)
13 Title of Roman emperors (6)
15 Severe; stern (6)
17 Person who receives office visitors (12)
20 Gemstones (5)
21 Someone who studies data (7)
22 Sanctity (8)
23 With the addition of (4)

Down

1 Branch of mechanics (8)
2 Frame for holding an artist's work (5)
4 Habitual practice (6)
5 In accordance with general custom (12)
6 Italian sports car (7)
7 Welsh emblem (4)
8 Food shop (12)
12 Written laws (8)
14 Look something over closely (7)
16 Sprats (anag) (6)
18 Pastoral poem (5)
19 Luxurious; stylish (4)

CROSSWORD

No. 63

Across

1 Take as being true (6)
4 Keen insight (6)
9 Device that records the movements of someone (7)
10 Desiring what someone else has (7)
11 Network points where lines intersect (5)
12 Resay (anag) (5)
14 Distinguishing character (5)
15 Attach (5)
17 Semiconductor (5)
18 Precondition (7)
20 Unfasten (7)
21 Spirited horses (6)
22 Large property with land (6)

Down

1 Acclimatise or accustom (6)
2 Stalemate (5-3)
3 Creates (5)
5 Processions of vehicles (7)
6 Country where one finds Bamako (4)
7 Pokes gently (6)
8 Traitorous (11)
13 Self-operating machines (8)
14 Exhilarated (7)
15 Popular round fruits (6)
16 Building devoted to worship (6)
17 Eg mallards (5)
19 Look at amorously (4)

No. 64

Across

1 Seat (anag) (4)
3 Shields from (8)
9 Reverberating (7)
10 Fit with glass (5)
11 Unhappy (3)
12 Number in a trio (5)
13 Our planet (5)
15 Thin crisp biscuit (5)
17 Portable source of light (5)
18 Dandy (3)
19 Bits of meat of low value (5)
20 Of the stomach (7)
21 Prayer service (8)
22 Head covering (4)

Down

1 Hidden store of valuables (8,5)
2 Plant pest (5)
4 Shipyard worker (6)
5 Fellowship (12)
6 Burnt (7)
7 Lacking originality (13)
8 Orcas (6,6)
14 Tall quadruped (7)
16 Large bottle for wine (6)
18 Compel (5)

CROSSWORD

No. 65

Across

1 Puts down (4)
3 Gives a right to (8)
9 Severe mental suffering (7)
10 Arboreal primate (5)
11 Endures (5)
12 Wanderer (7)
13 Wolfgang ___ : Austrian composer (6)
15 Powerful (6)
17 Let in again (7)
18 Frenzied (5)
20 Decorate (5)
21 Relating to sight (7)
22 Catastrophe (8)
23 Mimic (4)

Down

1 The ___ / ___ : Fairy tale by Hans Christian Andersen (6,7)
2 Linear measures of three feet (5)
4 Indigenous (6)
5 Unlawful (12)
6 Back pain (7)
7 Tactically (13)
8 Calculations of dimensions (12)
14 Very enthusiastic (7)
16 Serving no functional purpose (6)
19 Tortilla topped with cheese (5)

No. 66

Across

1 Administrations (11)
9 Go in (5)
10 Large primate (3)
11 Singing voice (5)
12 Fight (3-2)
13 Mythical sea creatures (8)
16 Calling out (8)
18 Travels on a bicycle (5)
21 Parasitic insect (5)
22 Support for a golf ball (3)
23 Shadow (5)
24 Having contradictory outcomes (6-5)

Down

2 Lead batsmen (cricket) (7)
3 Endless (7)
4 Tented (anag) (6)
5 Acquires through merit (5)
6 Short treatise (5)
7 Immoderate (11)
8 Try to predict an outcome (6-5)
14 Foolish person (7)
15 Share information (7)
17 Limp (6)
19 ___ Maradona: footballer (5)
20 Small firework (5)

CROSSWORD

No. 67

Across

7 Antenna (6)
8 Miner (6)
9 A Crown document (4)
10 Provider (8)
11 Cleaned its feathers (of a bird) (7)
13 Refine metal (5)
15 Bring about (5)
16 Companion (7)
18 Relating to speech sounds (8)
19 Pack down tightly (4)
21 East ___ : where one finds Norfolk (6)
22 Investigated in detail (6)

Down

1 Scorch (4)
2 Upsettingly (13)
3 Hero of the Odyssey (7)
4 Change; modify (5)
5 Assemblage (13)
6 Drove back (8)
12 Arriving at a destination (8)
14 General idea (7)
17 Drinking tube (5)
20 Overly submissive (4)

No. 68

Across

1 Sit with legs wide apart (8)
5 Recedes (4)
9 Bivalve marine molluscs (5)
10 Gena Lee ___ : Baywatch actress (5)
11 Betrothal (10)
14 Gets together (6)
15 Process food (6)
17 Metaphorical (10)
20 Mark of insertion (5)
21 Precious stone (5)
22 Fathers (4)
23 Item of additional book matter (8)

Down

1 Unwell (4)
2 Highway (4)
3 Break up into pieces (12)
4 Immature insects (6)
6 Had faith in (8)
7 Quality of being holy (8)
8 Hard to fathom (12)
12 Came to light (8)
13 Green-___ : good at gardening (8)
16 Gazed at (6)
18 Network of lines (4)
19 Shut with force (4)

CROSSWORD

No. 69

Across

1 Brief (4)
3 Game of chance (5,3)
9 Person proposed for office (7)
10 Money (5)
11 Section of a long poem (5)
12 Pin in a spinning wheel (7)
13 Get away from (6)
15 Form-fitting garment (6)
17 Had faith in (7)
18 Showing a willingness to achieve results (3-2)
20 Many times (5)
21 Exerts control over (7)
22 Made unhappy (8)
23 Catch sight of (4)

Down

1 Characterised by great care (13)
2 From the capital of Italy (5)
4 Anxious (6)
5 Children's toy (12)
6 Periods of ten years (7)
7 Affectedly (13)
8 Ineptness (12)
14 Wooed (7)
16 Regard with approval (6)
19 Facial protuberances (5)

No. 70

Across

1 Crude (5)
4 Toxins (7)
7 Produce a literary work (5)
8 Impending (8)
9 Hand shovel (5)
11 Intentionally hidden (8)
15 Strong type of coffee (8)
17 Bonds of union (5)
19 Orange plant pigment (8)
20 Bed cover (5)
21 Learned (7)
22 Deducts (5)

Down

1 Strangely (9)
2 Horizontal angle of a compass bearing (7)
3 Backdrop; landscape (7)
4 Quickly (6)
5 Morsels of food (6)
6 Observed (5)
10 Mistaken (9)
12 Marched (7)
13 Characterised by severe self-discipline (7)
14 Fable (6)
16 Sculptured figure (6)
18 Opposite one of two (5)

No. 71

Across

1 Volcano in Sicily (4)
3 Alluring (8)
9 Dry red table wine of Italy (7)
10 Restore factory settings (5)
11 Mathematics of triangles (12)
13 List of ingredients for a dish (6)
15 Change rapidly from one position to another (6)
17 Showing gratitude (12)
20 Tiny piece of food (5)
21 Apparatus (7)
22 Critical explanation (8)
23 Extras (cricket) (4)

Down

1 And so on (2,6)
2 Makhaya ___ : South African cricketer (5)
4 Thomas Alva ___ : US inventor (6)
5 Persistence (12)
6 Sunrise (anag) (7)
7 Movable barrier (4)
8 Without equal (12)
12 Street cleaners (8)
14 Apprehend; snare (7)
16 Norway lobsters (6)
18 Frostily (5)
19 Throb; dull pain (4)

No. 72

Across

1 Greatly respect (6)
7 Deceptive (8)
8 Purpose (3)
9 Small chicken (6)
10 Adult male singing voice (4)
11 Make a physical or mental effort (5)
13 Country whose capital is Budapest (7)
15 Requests to God (7)
17 Small seat (5)
21 Image of a god (4)
22 Formal assessment (6)
23 Division of a play (3)
24 User; purchaser (8)
25 Over there (6)

Down

1 Relating to horses (6)
2 Multiply by three (6)
3 Merriment (5)
4 Glitz; allure (7)
5 Edible snail (8)
6 Depression from a meteor impact (6)
12 Monarchist (8)
14 Ancient galley (7)
16 Extremely fashionable; scalding (3-3)
18 Ahead (6)
19 Pillager (6)
20 All (5)

CROSSWORD

No. 73

Across

1 Sagacious (6)
4 Card game similar to whist (6)
9 Open area of grassland (7)
10 Necessary (7)
11 Awry; wrong (5)
12 Put in considerable effort (5)
14 Pond-dwelling amphibians (5)
15 ___ Arabia: country (5)
17 Grin (5)
18 Ancient wise king (7)
20 Cup (7)
21 Revolve (6)
22 Throes (anag) (6)

Down

1 Be attractive (6)
2 Expression of gratitude (5,3)
3 Lose a contest intentionally (5)
5 Anticipates (7)
6 Coloured ring of feathers on a bird (4)
7 Unemotional (6)
8 Goodwill (11)
13 Unending (8)
14 Product of the imagination (7)
15 Female sibling (6)
16 Rejuvenates (6)
17 Hurt; clever (5)
19 Plunder; take illegally (4)

No. 74

Across

7 Soothed; subsided (6)
8 Get by with what is available (4,2)
10 Birthplace of Napoleon (7)
11 Leans (5)
12 Therefore (4)
13 Rascal (5)
17 Sporting stadium (5)
18 Near (anag) (4)
22 Brief smell (5)
23 Opposite of thinner (7)
24 Looked searchingly (6)
25 Odour-releasing animals (6)

Down

1 Draws forth (7)
2 Sudden outburst of something (5-2)
3 Sticky sap (5)
4 Kind of music (7)
5 Stomach (5)
6 Cause to stop sleeping (5)
9 Inoculate (9)
14 Moved slowly with the current (7)
15 Speaking (7)
16 Act of entering (7)
19 Brushed clean (5)
20 Underground worker (5)
21 Suave and smooth (of a person) (5)

CROSSWORD

No. 75

Across

1 Open a wine bottle (6)
7 Worm (8)
8 Hurried (3)
9 Demands; insists on (6)
10 Black waterbird (4)
11 Exit (5)
13 Young children (7)
15 Digits (7)
17 Welsh breed of dog (5)
21 Affirm with confidence (4)
22 Bowed string instruments (6)
23 Be in debt (3)
24 An indirect implication (8)
25 Stinging weed (6)

Down

1 Imaginary (6)
2 Where one watches films (6)
3 Bump (5)
4 Funny (7)
5 Ascot cat (anag) (8)
6 Clever or skilful (6)
12 Strong; full of energy (8)
14 Stop from occurring (7)
16 Make something new (6)
18 Place that is frequented for holidays (6)
19 Hinder (6)
20 Subatomic particle (5)

No. 76

Across

1 Settle a hotel bill on leaving (5,3)
5 Skilful (4)
8 Country in SE Asia (5)
9 Get rid of (7)
10 Communal settlement in Israel (7)
12 Capable of being dissolved (7)
14 Bodyguards (7)
16 Sets out on a journey (7)
18 Japanese massage technique (7)
19 Spacious (5)
20 Delves into (4)
21 Substantial (8)

Down

1 Caribbean country (4)
2 Reprimand (6)
3 Tailless Australian marsupial (5,4)
4 John ___ : US novelist (6)
6 Exit; Bible book (6)
7 Small pincers (8)
11 Miscellaneous objects of little value (4-1-4)
12 Accented (8)
13 Flowing back (6)
14 Old Portuguese currency (6)
15 Take away (6)
17 Stringed instrument (4)

CROSSWORD

No. 77

Across

7 Bearlike (6)
8 Czech monetary unit (6)
10 Crafty; cunning (7)
11 Side of a large object (5)
12 Uncommon (4)
13 Loft (5)
17 Submerged ridges of rock (5)
18 Tiny amount (4)
22 Skilled job (5)
23 Car motors (7)
24 Expelled from office (6)
25 Unit of money (6)

Down

1 Overthrow covertly (7)
2 Stablemen (7)
3 Unfasten a garment (5)
4 Penalty (7)
5 Immature insects (5)
6 Songbirds (5)
9 Gives evidence in court (9)
14 Lend set (anag) (7)
15 Advocate (7)
16 Officer in the armed forces (7)
19 Stage performer (5)
20 Slight error of judgement (5)
21 ___ on: urged; encouraged (5)

No. 78

Across

1 Legendary story (4)
3 Complete; utter (8)
9 Stringed instruments (7)
10 Neck warmer (5)
11 Conclude (5)
12 South America country (7)
13 Relations by marriage (2-4)
15 Stick of wax (6)
17 Get as one's own (7)
18 Invigorating medicine (5)
20 Epic poem ascribed to Homer (5)
21 Eg from Moscow (7)
22 Plummet (8)
23 Item of footwear (4)

Down

1 Enlargement (13)
2 Robber (5)
4 Measure of capacity for corn (6)
5 Obfuscation (12)
6 Without help (7)
7 Fizz (13)
8 Lacking tolerance or flexibility (6-6)
14 Fluids (7)
16 History play by Shakespeare (5,1)
19 Horse's cry (5)

CROSSWORD

No. 79

Across

1 Develop (6)
4 Disturbance (6)
9 Shade of red (7)
10 Blood relative (7)
11 Floating platforms (5)
12 Measures duration (5)
14 Harass; frustrate (5)
15 Appear suddenly (3,2)
17 Anaesthetic (5)
18 Stations where journeys end (7)
20 Argued against (7)
21 Sphere; territory (6)
22 Overflows its banks (of a river) (6)

Down

1 Straighten out (6)
2 Light sandal (4-4)
3 Slips (anag) (5)
5 Capricious (7)
6 Roster (4)
7 Songlike cries (6)
8 Preference; liking (11)
13 Exaggerated masculinity (8)
14 Relating to knowledge based on deduction (1,6)
15 Placed a plant in a container (6)
16 Wears away (6)
17 Kick out (5)
19 Wander (4)

CROSSWORD

No. 80

Across

1 Performing on stage (6)
7 Importance; stress (8)
8 Flightless bird (3)
9 Breakfast food (6)
10 Long flowing hair (4)
11 Stage name of Mark Althavean Andrews (5)
13 Unity (7)
15 Attack (7)
17 Name applied to something (5)
21 Soothing ointment (4)
22 Crowd (6)
23 Fellow (3)
24 All people (8)
25 Chest (6)

Down

1 Wards off (6)
2 Outdoes (6)
3 Large waterbirds (5)
4 Choices (7)
5 State of Australia (8)
6 Very tall mythical beings (6)
12 Bog (8)
14 Military unit (7)
16 Deprive of food (6)
18 Mendicant (6)
19 Voice box (6)
20 Welcome (5)

CROSSWORD

No. 81

Across

7 Feeling a continuous dull pain (6)
8 Whole (6)
10 Pasta pockets (7)
11 Major artery (5)
12 Midday (4)
13 Taming of the ___ : Shakespeare play (5)
17 Admirable (5)
18 Bate (anag) (4)
22 Angry (5)
23 Dismissing from a job (7)
24 Sailing barge (6)
25 Number in a football team (6)

Down

1 Jolting (7)
2 V-shaped mark (7)
3 Representative; messenger (5)
4 Breathed in (7)
5 Unite in matrimony (5)
6 Mammal of the weasel family (5)
9 Blind (9)
14 Containing no water at all (4,3)
15 Accept to be true (7)
16 Line that touches a curve (7)
19 Opinions (5)
20 Fruits of the palm (5)
21 Burn with hot liquid (5)

No. 82

Across

1 Chef (4)
3 Transport systems (8)
9 Foreboding (7)
10 Tremulous sound (5)
11 Andrew Lloyd Webber musical (5)
12 Plant of the buttercup family (7)
13 Compel by intimidation (6)
15 Expedition to see animals (6)
17 Approximately (7)
18 Visual representation (5)
20 Up to the time when (5)
21 Bridgelike structure (7)
22 Traitor (8)
23 Large group of people (4)

Down

1 Type of surveillance system (6-7)
2 Small antelope (5)
4 Scoundrel (6)
5 Relating to numbers (12)
6 US state (7)
7 Obviously (4-9)
8 Not intoxicating (of a drink) (12)
14 Imaginary line around the earth (7)
16 ___ Plath: author of The Bell Jar (6)
19 Sky-blue colour (5)

CROSSWORD

No. 83

Across

1 Decorated with a raised design (8)
5 Leguminous plant (4)
9 More mature (5)
10 Snail (anag) (5)
11 Science of analysing data (10)
14 Potassium compound (6)
15 Pear-shaped fruit (6)
17 Culmination (10)
20 Beer (5)
21 Assumed appearance (5)
22 Opposite of light (4)
23 Two-wheeled vehicles (8)

Down

1 Seal of the Archbishop of York (4)
2 Tenders (4)
3 Atmospheric layer (12)
4 Official proclamations (6)
6 Views about something (8)
7 Aided (8)
8 Modestly (12)
12 Horrified (8)
13 More powerful (8)
16 Dwarfed tree (6)
18 Tablet (4)
19 Female chickens (4)

No. 84

Across

1 Too; in addition (4)
3 Wide-ranging (8)
9 More than one (7)
10 Try out (5)
11 Steal (3)
12 Join together (5)
13 English cricket ground (5)
15 Country in the Middle East (5)
17 Levels out (5)
18 Small amount of something (3)
19 Avoid (danger) (5)
20 Hurtful (7)
21 Finance department (8)
22 Extravagant publicity (4)

Down

1 Paid announcement (13)
2 Clean thoroughly (5)
4 Small ring fixed between two surfaces (6)
5 Eager (12)
6 Existing at the beginning (7)
7 50th anniversary of a major event (6,7)
8 Vagrancy (12)
14 Introductory piece of music (7)
16 Eg Eminem (6)
18 Silly (5)

CROSSWORD

No. 85

Across

7 Be preoccupied with a topic (6)
8 Erase (6)
10 Selfishness (7)
11 Piles (5)
12 Be at a ___ : be puzzled (4)
13 Thin pancake (5)
17 Measure heaviness (5)
18 Group of three (4)
22 Do really well at (5)
23 Recites as a chant (7)
24 Silly tricks (6)
25 Ignores completely (6)

Down

1 European river (7)
2 Choose and follow (7)
3 Up and about (5)
4 Fashion anew (7)
5 US state whose capital is Austin (5)
6 Uptight (5)
9 Natalie ___ : Australian singer (9)
14 Reticular (7)
15 Cutting back a tree (7)
16 Be composed of (7)
19 High-pitched noises (5)
20 Go away from quickly (5)
21 Avocet-like wader (5)

No. 86

Across

7 Vend again (6)
8 Homes (6)
9 Axelike tool (4)
10 Lack of intensity (8)
11 At a greater distance (7)
13 Clothing made from denim (5)
15 Ways or tracks (5)
16 Treachery (7)
18 Symmetrical open plane curve (8)
19 Imperial unit (4)
21 Move back (6)
22 Robberies (6)

Down

1 Alcoholic drink (4)
2 State of extreme happiness (7,6)
3 More slender (7)
4 Ahead of time (5)
5 Forger (13)
6 Argued logically (8)
12 Without warning (8)
14 People who insist on sticking to formal rules (7)
17 Desires (5)
20 Domestic felines (4)

CROSSWORD

No. 87

Across

1 Remove the skin from (4)
3 Astronaut (8)
9 Deliver by parachute (3-4)
10 Vertical part of a step (5)
11 Inspiring action (12)
13 Holds one's ground (6)
15 Martial art (4,2)
17 Sleepwalker (12)
20 Capital of Vietnam (5)
21 Large fast warship (7)
22 Make information known (8)
23 Halt (4)

Down

1 Composer of a sacred song (8)
2 Small heron (5)
4 Small songbirds (6)
5 Type of cloud (12)
6 Small hardy range horse (7)
7 Standard (4)
8 Fortunate; opportune (12)
12 Flatter (6,2)
14 Quantities (7)
16 Hits hard (6)
18 Tines (anag) (5)
19 Low dull sound (4)

No. 88

Across

1 By some margin; easily (11)
9 Consumer (5)
10 22nd Greek letter (3)
11 Totally erases (5)
12 Ire (5)
13 Stealing (cattle) (8)
16 In a friendly manner (8)
18 Idiotic (5)
21 Camera image (5)
22 Uncooked (of meat) (3)
23 Send money (5)
24 Positives and negatives (4,3,4)

Down

2 Distant settlement (7)
3 Newly (7)
4 Share out food sparingly (6)
5 Pointed projectile (5)
6 City in Tuscany (5)
7 Eg Huw Edwards and Fiona Bruce (11)
8 The rules of the road (7,4)
14 Cynic (7)
15 Insect body segment (7)
17 Crazy person (6)
19 Strength (5)
20 Threads or fibres (5)

CROSSWORD

No. 89

Across

7 Domestic assistant (2,4)
8 Holds and uses a tool (6)
9 Meat from a cow (4)
10 Large African mammals (8)
11 Land retained by a lord (7)
13 Of definite shape (5)
15 Lean or thin (5)
16 Disperse (7)
18 Sport popular in America (8)
19 Tehran is the capital here (4)
21 Young hog (6)
22 Portions of a play (6)

Down

1 Light toboggan (4)
2 Unenthusiastically (4-9)
3 Perennial herb (7)
4 Spin quickly (5)
5 Complete in itself (of a thing) (4-9)
6 Glue (8)
12 Definite and clear (8)
14 Type of optician (7)
17 ___ Brooks: US country singer (5)
20 Inspires fear (4)

No. 90

Across

7 Metamorphic rock (6)
8 Noisily (6)
10 Get rid of something (7)
11 Group of shots (5)
12 Require (4)
13 Objection; complain (5)
17 Large waterbird (5)
18 Public school (4)
22 Pulsate (5)
23 Type of sovereign (7)
24 Short track for storing trains (6)
25 Straighten out (6)

Down

1 Shock with wonder (7)
2 Moved (7)
3 Famous English racetrack (5)
4 Spreads rumours (7)
5 Mix up; confuse (5)
6 Mike ___ : US boxer (5)
9 One to whom a letter is directed (9)
14 Crying heavily (7)
15 Promising young actress (7)
16 Trespass (7)
19 Hiding place (5)
20 Groom's partner (5)
21 Rotates (5)

CROSSWORD

No. 91

Across

1 Pieces of jewellery (8)
5 Short tail (4)
8 Punctuation mark (5)
9 Shoulder blade (7)
10 Stimulates; provokes (7)
12 ___ Crowe: Gladiator actor (7)
14 Live longer than (7)
16 Weasel-like animal (7)
18 Copy (7)
19 Frozen fruit juice on a stick (5)
20 Neither good nor bad (2-2)
21 Walked about (8)

Down

1 Stride; single step (4)
2 Type of rain cloud (6)
3 Showing no enthusiasm (9)
4 Adornment of hanging threads (6)
6 Eg Hampshire or Berkshire (6)
7 Send a signal (8)
11 Cut short (9)
12 Defensive walls (8)
13 Slants (6)
14 Capital of Canada (6)
15 Person who fishes (6)
17 Stained a fabric or hair (4)

No. 92

Across

7 Spanish title for a married woman (6)
8 ___ and dining: entertaining well (6)
9 Hard hit cricket shot (4)
10 Freed from an obligation (8)
11 Tropical disease (7)
13 Lag behind (5)
15 Self-respect (5)
16 Temporary way of dealing with a problem (7)
18 Essential or fundamental (8)
19 Mite (anag) (4)
21 London suburb (6)
22 Strong public protest (6)

Down

1 Transaction (4)
2 Crude but effective (5,3,5)
3 Spear thrown in athletics (7)
4 Bird sound; chirp (5)
5 Not suitable (13)
6 Aromatic plant used in cooking (8)
12 Put in order (8)
14 Rich white cheese (7)
17 Imbibe (5)
20 Currency of Italy and Spain (4)

CROSSWORD

No. 93

Across

1 Bloodsucking insect (4)
3 Flight of steps (8)
9 Ancient large storage jar (7)
10 Too bright in colour (5)
11 Heavy long-handled tool (12)
13 Apprehend someone (6)
15 Steal; seize suddenly (6)
17 Made (12)
20 Flour dough used in cooking (5)
21 ___ Wilson: 28th US President (7)
22 Come together (8)
23 ___ Blyton: writer (4)

Down

1 Conduct business (8)
2 Small woodland (5)
4 Of inferior quality (6)
5 Clarification (12)
6 Hottest (7)
7 Jedi Master in Star Wars films (4)
8 Pay tribute to another (12)
12 Followed a person closely (8)
14 Secret affair (7)
16 Small insect (6)
18 Broadcast again (5)
19 Long narrative poem (4)

No. 94

Across

7 Expression of praise (6)
8 Centre (6)
10 Upstart (7)
11 Mental impressions (5)
12 Pubs (4)
13 Employing (5)
17 Start (5)
18 Release; give out (4)
22 Discard; throw away (5)
23 Group of figures representing a scene (7)
24 Meal (6)
25 Soul; spirit (6)

Down

1 Feeling of hopelessness (7)
2 Making a loud sound (7)
3 Unpleasant giants (5)
4 Apparitions (7)
5 Lazy person; layabout (5)
6 Extravagant meal (5)
9 Fringes of a city (9)
14 Best pod (anag) (7)
15 Call the validity of a practice into question (7)
16 Fruit pastry (7)
19 Russian sovereigns (5)
20 Stage items (5)
21 Bottomless pit (5)

CROSSWORD

No. 95

Across

1 Middle Eastern language (6)
7 Friendly (8)
8 Queen ___ : fairy in Romeo and Juliet (3)
9 Sloping (of a typeface) (6)
10 Ark builder (4)
11 Enamel-coated structure (5)
13 Topmost (7)
15 Coarsen (anag) (7)
17 Willow twig (5)
21 Round before the final (abbrev) (4)
22 Guardian (6)
23 Epoch (3)
24 Easy chair (8)
25 Good luck charm (6)

Down

1 Very nearly (6)
2 Having colourless skin (6)
3 Strong thick rope (5)
4 Cookie (7)
5 Propels with force (8)
6 Makes a weak cry (of sheep) (6)
12 Substantial; not elusive (8)
14 Disguising; hiding (7)
16 Complied with orders (6)
18 Country in the Middle East (6)
19 Happen again (6)
20 ___ firma: dry land (5)

No. 96

Across

1 Boiled pudding (4)
3 Destined to fail (3-5)
9 Word having the same meaning as another (7)
10 Aqualung (5)
11 Friend (Spanish) (5)
12 Greed (7)
13 Particularly strong ability (6)
15 Newspaper boss (6)
17 Item of furniture (7)
18 Total disorder (5)
20 Huge (5)
21 Clothing (7)
22 Christmas season (8)
23 Tax (4)

Down

1 Repugnantly (13)
2 Spore-producing organisms (5)
4 Assumed propositions (6)
5 Popular takeaway food (4,3,5)
6 Holiday visitor (7)
7 Completely (opposed) (13)
8 Formal notice (12)
14 Towards the side (7)
16 Drive aground (a boat) (6)
19 Vigour and spirit (5)

CROSSWORD

No. 97

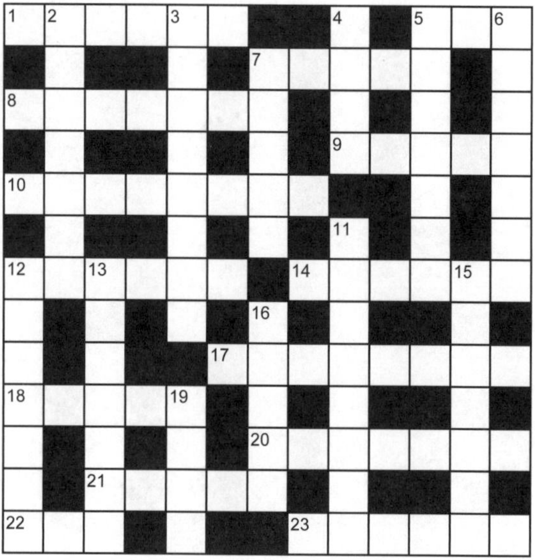

Across

1 Fine; great (6)
5 Give a nickname to (3)
7 Arose from slumber (5)
8 Jostled (7)
9 Talk (5)
10 Biscuit that contains almonds (8)
12 Wild animals (6)
14 Arm muscle (6)
17 Range of colours (8)
18 Humiliate (5)
20 Turned down (7)
21 Beguile (5)
22 Gradation of colour (3)
23 Begins (6)

Down

2 Instruct (7)
3 Exuberant merriment (8)
4 Male children (4)
5 Merit (7)
6 Business deal makers (7)
7 Supplementary component (3-2)
11 Reduction in price (8)
12 Width (7)
13 Make progress (7)
15 Judicious (7)
16 Sudden contraction (5)
19 Energy and enthusiasm (4)

No. 98

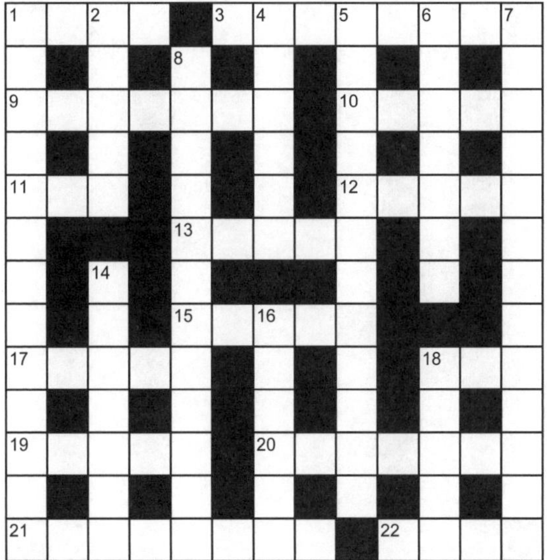

Across

1 Father (4)
3 Happy ___ : card game (8)
9 Plunderers (7)
10 Record on tape (5)
11 Measure of length (3)
12 Lawful (5)
13 Synthetic fabric (5)
15 Underground enlarged stem (5)
17 Semiaquatic mammal (5)
18 Sense of self-esteem (3)
19 Maladroit (5)
20 Eg primrose and lemon (7)
21 Teaching (8)
22 Extremely (4)

Down

1 One with extremely high standards (13)
2 Bottle (5)
4 Descend down a rock face (6)
5 Immune (12)
6 Admits formally to a post (7)
7 Impulsively (13)
8 One who takes part in a protest (12)
14 Backtrack (7)
16 Subatomic particle such as a nucleon (6)
18 Run away with a lover (5)

CROSSWORD

No. 99

Across

1 Action of ending a partnership (11)
9 Rice dish (5)
10 Introverted (3)
11 Track of an animal (5)
12 Beads (anag) (5)
13 Created in the house (8)
16 Sleep disorder (8)
18 Period of keeping awake to pray (5)
21 One of the United Arab Emirates (5)
22 ___ Thurman: actress (3)
23 Headdress worn by a bishop (5)
24 Rural scenery (11)

Down

2 Imparts knowledge (7)
3 Most important (7)
4 Drooped (6)
5 Pollex (5)
6 Expels from a position (5)
7 Harmful and sneaky (11)
8 Act of publishing in several places (11)
14 Is curious about (7)
15 Helped to happen (7)
17 Chatter (6)
19 Bird droppings used as fertiliser (5)
20 SI unit of luminous flux (5)

CROSSWORD

No. 100

Across

- **7** Festival (6)
- **8** Yellow fruit (6)
- **9** Island of the Inner Hebrides (4)
- **10** Relating to critical explanation (8)
- **11** Subsiding (7)
- **13** European country (5)
- **15** Bitterly pungent (5)
- **16** Prompts (7)
- **18** Lecture forcefully (8)
- **19** Brood (4)
- **21** Beat soundly (6)
- **22** Learned person (6)

Down

- **1** Eg the colour of salmon (4)
- **2** Capable of being found out (13)
- **3** Inns (7)
- **4** Woodwind instruments (5)
- **5** Amusement (13)
- **6** Unnamed (8)
- **12** Card game (8)
- **14** Acknowledgement of payment (7)
- **17** Unconditional love (5)
- **20** Proper (4)

CROSSWORD

No. 101

Across

1 Appointed member of the House of Lords (4,4)
5 Sparkling wine (4)
9 ___ Mortensen: actor (5)
10 Receive a ball in one's hands (5)
11 Edible (10)
14 Recount (6)
15 Hawk (6)
17 Meaningless or confusing language (5,5)
20 Eighth Greek letter (5)
21 Anxiety (5)
22 Apex or peak (4)
23 Tree of the birch family (8)

Down

1 Deep affection (4)
2 Obscures (4)
3 Commensurate (12)
4 Creepier (6)
6 Protein that neutralises an antigen (8)
7 Eg Usain Bolt and Mo Farah (8)
8 Disorganised person (12)
12 Having a strong smell (8)
13 Mountaineers (8)
16 Unthinkingly eager (4-2)
18 Mythical creature (4)
19 Moat (anag) (4)

CROSSWORD

No. 102

Across

- **1** Slightly open (4)
- **3** Grandiosity of language (8)
- **9** Venetian boat (7)
- **10** Noble gas (5)
- **11** Blend together (3)
- **12** ___ flu: form of influenza (5)
- **13** Greek writer of fables (5)
- **15** Prohibit (5)
- **17** ___ Adkins: singer (5)
- **18** Hip (anag) (3)
- **19** Form of humour (5)
- **20** Fragrant gum or spice (7)
- **21** Recondite (8)
- **22** ___ Barlow: Take That singer (4)

Down

- **1** Given to debate (13)
- **2** Attach to (5)
- **4** Stashes away (6)
- **5** Clearness (12)
- **6** Gets back (7)
- **7** Successively (13)
- **8** Pungent gas used as a preservative (12)
- **14** Quivering singing effect (7)
- **16** Minimal bathing suit (6)
- **18** Bamboo-eating animal (5)

CROSSWORD

No. 103

Across

1 Give entirely to a cause (8)
5 Still to be paid (4)
9 Express; complete (5)
10 Creamy-white colour (5)
11 A very influential country (10)
14 Select (6)
15 ___ Bocelli: Italian operatic singer (6)
17 Featureless (of a place) (10)
20 Promotional wording (5)
21 Opposite of outer (5)
22 Circular movement of water (4)
23 Mesmerism (8)

Down

1 Medicine (4)
2 Facts and statistics collectively (4)
3 Restrict within limits (12)
4 Small hairpiece (6)
6 Beetle larva that bores into timber (8)
7 Dawn (8)
8 Exemption from a rule (12)
12 Scrawl (8)
13 Enclosure (8)
16 Expensive (6)
18 Tiny social insects (4)
19 Undergarments (4)

CROSSWORD

No. 104

Across

7 Alcoholic drink (6)
8 Change direction suddenly (6)
9 Scottish lake (4)
10 Segment of the spinal column (8)
11 Become husky (7)
13 Paula ___ : US singer (5)
15 Game of chance (5)
16 A contest (7)
18 Looked for (8)
19 Mate (anag) (4)
21 Keep hold of (6)
22 Excessively casual (6)

Down

1 Joan ___ : Spanish artist (4)
2 Tyrannical; domineering (13)
3 Trailer (7)
4 Take the place of (5)
5 Resonance (13)
6 Orchestral piece at the beginning of an opera (8)
12 Device that measures distance travelled (8)
14 Least warm (7)
17 Collision; shift (5)
20 European mountain range (4)

No. 105

Across

1 Helper (4)
3 Term for a feline pet (8)
9 Agreement (7)
10 Fertile spot in a desert (5)
11 Act of removing restrictions (12)
13 Young person (6)
15 Playing period in polo (6)
17 Awkward (12)
20 Joining together with cord (5)
21 Tufted (7)
22 Spread out (8)
23 Fill or satiate (4)

Down

1 Mishap (8)
2 Person who eats in a restaurant (5)
4 Excessively (6)
5 Cheated someone financially (5-7)
6 Item of clerical clothing (7)
7 Throw a coin in the air (4)
8 Style of playing blues (6-6)
12 Routine and ordinary (3-2-3)
14 Experts (7)
16 Removes from one's property (6)
18 Praise enthusiastically (5)
19 Football boot grip (4)

No. 106

Across

1 Compositions in verse (5)
4 Brought about (7)
7 Scope or extent (5)
8 Thing that is easily done (8)
9 Try (5)
11 Slapdash (8)
15 Trained user of a machine (8)
17 Understood with certainty (5)
19 Constant movement backwards and forwards (2,3,3)
20 Parts (anag) (5)
21 ___ Down the Wind: musical (7)
22 Mountain range in South America (5)

Down

1 Nonsense (9)
2 Ugly building (7)
3 Parchment rolls (7)
4 Urges to do something (6)
5 Furthest; extreme (6)
6 ___ Dushku: actress (5)
10 Annuals (9)
12 Father of a parent (7)
13 Filled completely (7)
14 Pinches sharply (6)
16 ___ Buffay: character in Friends (6)
18 Indentation; nick (5)

CROSSWORD

No. 107

Across

1 Variants (8)
5 US state (4)
8 Electronic message (5)
9 Plant with bright flowers (7)
10 Enduring (7)
12 Sincere (7)
14 Tenth month of the year (7)
16 Turns around (on a chair) (7)
18 Deficiency of red blood cells (7)
19 Gains possession of (5)
20 Spool-like toy (2-2)
21 Respected and admired (8)

Down

1 Swerve (4)
2 Ronald ___ : former US President (6)
3 Unreadable (9)
4 Gnaw (6)
6 Substance found in wine (6)
7 Eg hats and helmets (8)
11 Small carved figure (9)
12 Alphabetical list of terms (8)
13 Involving pairs (6)
14 Academy Awards (6)
15 Insincere talk (6)
17 Sued (anag) (4)

No. 108

Across

1 ___ Major: the Great Bear (4)
3 Meeting where instructions are given (8)
9 Tardiest (7)
10 Managed (5)
11 Someone who sets up their own business (12)
13 Person who acts for another (6)
15 Horse restraint (6)
17 Nationally (12)
20 A clearing in a wood (5)
21 Seven-a-side game (7)
22 Re-evaluate (8)
23 Mosh (anag) (4)

Down

1 Unstable (8)
2 Dark beer (5)
4 Yield or make (a profit) (6)
5 Behavioural peculiarity (12)
6 Seize and take legal custody of (7)
7 Deities (4)
8 Notwithstanding (12)
12 Uses again (8)
14 Proportionately (3,4)
16 Fixed periods of work (6)
18 Animal restraint (5)
19 Jelly or culture medium (4)

CROSSWORD

No. 109

Across

1 Thin strip of wood (4)
3 Writs or warrants (8)
9 Fourth book of the Bible (7)
10 Agree or correspond (5)
11 Terrified or extremely shocked (6-6)
13 Slow to understand (6)
15 Wrongdoer (6)
17 Tricky elements; obstacles (12)
20 Foot-operated lever (5)
21 Bodies of writing (7)
22 Quotidian (8)
23 Pass (anag) (4)

Down

1 Formal meal (8)
2 Type of stopwatch (5)
4 Oppose (6)
5 Butterfly larvae (12)
6 Large web-footed bird (7)
7 Utters (4)
8 Regretfully (12)
12 Solids with regularly ordered atoms (8)
14 Twirl (7)
16 Spiny tree or shrub (6)
18 People who are greatly admired (5)
19 Recess (4)

No. 110

Across

1 Mineral of lead sulphide (6)
7 Type of pasta (8)
8 Mythical monster (3)
9 Each (6)
10 Metal fastener (4)
11 Last Greek letter (5)
13 Flog; whip (7)
15 Set apart (7)
17 Short high-pitched tone (5)
21 Child who has no home (4)
22 Very fine substance (6)
23 Deer (3)
24 Greek dish (8)
25 Renovate (6)

Down

1 Small cave (6)
2 Find (6)
3 ___ Valletta: actress (5)
4 Eg biology (7)
5 Peaceful (8)
6 Finishing (6)
12 Type of Eurasian carp (8)
14 Idealistic (7)
16 Part of a motor (6)
18 Archimedes' famous cry (6)
19 Gather or collect (4,2)
20 Give a solemn oath (5)

CROSSWORD

No. 111

Across

1 Relating to monkeys (6)
5 Writing fluid (3)
7 Earnest appeals (5)
8 Marks of a zebra (7)
9 Monastery superior (5)
10 Gloomily (8)
12 Feels upset and annoyed (6)
14 Remains preserved in rock (6)
17 Wild prank (8)
18 Steered a car (5)
20 Vital content (7)
21 Country whose capital is Sana'a (5)
22 Jewel (3)
23 Birthplace of St Francis (6)

Down

2 Time between events (7)
3 Harshness of tone (8)
4 Sixth Greek letter (4)
5 Lines of equal pressure on maps (7)
6 Small falcon (7)
7 Sacred hymn or song (5)
11 Bogs or marshes (8)
12 Moving smoothly (7)
13 Kind of abbreviation (7)
15 Brings about (7)
16 Anaemic-looking (5)
19 Trees of the genus Ulmus (4)

No. 112

Across

7 Cooperation (13)
8 Put forward an idea (8)
9 Mammal with antlers (4)
10 Mottled (7)
12 Absolute (5)
14 Love intently (5)
16 Plans to do something (7)
19 Protective crust over a wound (4)
20 Dejected (8)
22 Compiler of a dictionary (13)

Down

1 Number after three (4)
2 Sumptuous and large (of a meal) (4-2)
3 Embarrassed (7)
4 Assess (5)
5 Workplace for an artist (6)
6 Tennis stroke (8)
11 Physiologically dependent (8)
13 Responses (7)
15 ___ Williams: singer (6)
17 Unless (6)
18 Goodbye (Spanish) (5)
21 Plant stalk (4)

CROSSWORD

No. 113

Across

1 Group of singers (5)
4 Smashes into another vehicle (7)
7 Spiked weapon (5)
8 Ringing in the ears (8)
9 Examined furtively (5)
11 Arguments (8)
15 Raised horizontal surface (8)
17 Harsh and serious (5)
19 Safety restraint in a car (4,4)
20 Passageway (5)
21 Roof flue (7)
22 Period of darkness (5)

Down

1 Literary analyses (9)
2 Relating to Oxford (7)
3 Mediterranean resort area (7)
4 Offhand (6)
5 Majestic (6)
6 Delete (5)
10 One who writes plays (9)
12 Hat with a wide brim (7)
13 Horse's fodder container (7)
14 Type of examination (6)
16 Margin of safety (6)
18 Upper part of the leg (5)

No. 114

Across

1 Mire (anag) (4)
3 Approximate (8)
9 Divide into three parts (7)
10 Weatherproof coat (5)
11 Knocks into (5)
12 Imposing a tax (7)
13 Units of linear measure (6)
15 Cheese shredder (6)
17 Receiver (7)
18 Trick or feat of daring (5)
20 Expel from a country (5)
21 On the sheltered side (7)
22 Medicine (8)
23 TV award (4)

Down

1 Institution (13)
2 Phrase that is not taken literally (5)
4 End a dispute (6)
5 Made poor (12)
6 Aerial rescue (7)
7 In an inflated manner (13)
8 Re-evaluation (12)
14 War trumpet (7)
16 Less fresh (of bread) (6)
19 Deprive of weapons (5)

CROSSWORD

No. 115

Across

1 ___ Stewart: ex-England cricketer (4)
3 Straightens out (8)
9 Undergarments (7)
10 Conical tent (5)
11 Make imperfect (3)
12 Egg-shaped solid (5)
13 Furnish or supply (5)
15 Concealed; secret (5)
17 Declare invalid (5)
18 Feline (3)
19 Needing to be scratched (5)
20 Slope (7)
21 Male relation (8)
22 Seek (anag) (4)

Down

1 Easy to deal with (13)
2 Mistake (5)
4 Capital of the Bahamas (6)
5 Branch of astronomy (12)
6 Hires a new member of staff (7)
7 Loyalty in the face of trouble (13)
8 Working for oneself (4-8)
14 Remedy for everything (7)
16 Deep blue colour (6)
18 Become suddenly understandable (5)

No. 116

Across

7 Flimsy (13)
8 Formal agreement (8)
9 Not odd (4)
10 Primarily (7)
12 Trembling poplar (5)
14 Large amounts of land (5)
16 Ill-mannered (7)
19 Seize (4)
20 Pattern of circular spots (5,3)
22 Advertising by telephone (13)

Down

1 Knowledge (abbrev) (4)
2 Measuring sticks (6)
3 Attacks (7)
4 Written agreements (5)
5 Soaks in liquid (6)
6 Monotony (8)
11 Made subject to (8)
13 Resembling a deity (7)
15 Symbol or representation (6)
17 Cooks in the oven (6)
18 Disgust (5)
21 Possesses (4)

CROSSWORD

No. 117

Across

1 Wine container (8)
5 Lies (anag) (4)
8 Deep fissure (5)
9 John ___ : former US tennis star (7)
10 Male TV announcers (7)
12 Thin flat unleavened biscuit (7)
14 Not thorough (7)
16 Encode (7)
18 Sellers (7)
19 Dramatic musical work (5)
20 Reckless; hasty (4)
21 Ozzy ___ : Black Sabbath vocalist (8)

Down

1 Eg a mallard (4)
2 Item of neckwear (6)
3 In name only (9)
4 Fur of a stoat (6)
6 Economise (6)
7 Infinite time (8)
11 Sport played in a pool (5,4)
12 Person who sees something (8)
13 Small rounded cakes (6)
14 Stagnation or inactivity (6)
15 Occupation or profession (6)
17 Having a sound mind (4)

No. 118

Across

- **7** Treelike grass (6)
- **8** Storage space for a car (6)
- **9** Russian sovereign (4)
- **10** Show to be correct (8)
- **11** Gather (7)
- **13** Strike (5)
- **15** Meat and vegetables on a skewer (5)
- **16** Cyclone (7)
- **18** Recurring at intervals (8)
- **19** Religious sisters (4)
- **21** Basic metrical unit in a poem (6)
- **22** Experience again (6)

Down

- **1** Natural oily substances (4)
- **2** Shortened forms of words (13)
- **3** Able to pay one's debts (7)
- **4** Nimble (5)
- **5** Principally (13)
- **6** Excited or annoyed (8)
- **12** Small-scale musical drama (8)
- **14** Food eaten at a cinema (7)
- **17** ___ Allan Poe: US writer (5)
- **20** Area of a church (4)

CROSSWORD

No. 119

Across

1 Subatomic particle such as an electron (6)
4 Material; textile (6)
9 Reindeer (7)
10 White and lustrous (hair) (7)
11 Explode (5)
12 Garment worn in the kitchen (5)
14 Sulks (5)
15 Lively Bohemian dance (5)
17 Freedom from war (5)
18 Move something; agitate (7)
20 Terse (7)
21 Make beloved (6)
22 Loan shark (6)

Down

1 Composite fungus and alga (6)
2 European country (8)
3 Circle a planet (5)
5 Flowering shrubs (7)
6 Loose flowing garment (4)
7 Deep gorge (6)
8 Vulnerable to (11)
13 Rain tree (anag) (8)
14 Polish dance (7)
15 Oar (6)
16 Swordsman (6)
17 Eats like a bird (5)
19 Beach constituent (4)

No. 120

1		2		3		4		■	5	6		7
	■		■		■		■	■	■		■	
8					■	9						
	■		■		■		■	■	■		■	
■	■		■		■	10		11				
12							■		■		■	
	■	■	■		■	■	■		■	■	■	
	■	13	■		■	14				15		
16							■		■		■	■
	■		■	■	■		■		■		■	17
18							■	19				
	■		■	■	■		■		■		■	
20				■	21							

Across

1 Seriously (8)
5 Grows old (4)
8 Pointed part of a fork (5)
9 Harmful (7)
10 All together (2,5)
12 Timid (7)
14 Medical practitioners (7)
16 Piece of furniture (7)
18 Pear-shaped fruit (7)
19 Lazes; does nothing (5)
20 One of two equal parts (4)
21 Makes remote; cuts off (8)

Down

1 Drains of energy (4)
2 Lets go of (6)
3 Makes larger (9)
4 Horizontal supporting beam (6)
6 Slick and shiny (6)
7 Stops temporarily (8)
11 Fickle (9)
12 Washing basin in the garden (8)
13 Pull back from (6)
14 Sags (6)
15 Medium-sized feline (6)
17 Egyptian goddess of fertility (4)

CROSSWORD

No. 121

Across

1 Stringed musical instrument (8)
5 Splendid display (4)
8 Show triumphant joy (5)
9 Omission of a sound when speaking (7)
10 Acquire from a relative (7)
12 Percussion instrument (7)
14 Type of handicraft (7)
16 Personal possession (7)
18 Examine (7)
19 US state (5)
20 People in general (4)
21 Actor (8)

Down

1 A fitting reward (4)
2 Not masculine or feminine (6)
3 Furthest away from the centre (9)
4 Spain and Portugal (6)
6 Willow twigs (6)
7 Expressing remorse (8)
11 As likely to succeed as to fail (3-2-4)
12 Devilry (8)
13 Maiden (6)
14 Clasp (6)
15 US state of islands (6)
17 ___ out: very tired (4)

No. 122

Across

1 Walks up and down (5)
4 Writing implements (7)
7 Put out a fire (5)
8 Field game (8)
9 Unit of heat (5)
11 Made uniform (8)
15 ___ rose: climbing Chinese rose (8)
17 Opposite of old (5)
19 Distinction (8)
20 Grain storage chambers (5)
21 Adorn with precious stones (7)
22 ___ Izzard: comedian (5)

Down

1 Branch of knowledge (9)
2 Curved inwards (of a surface) (7)
3 Walks leisurely (7)
4 Chase (6)
5 Dress (6)
6 Opposite of a winner (5)
10 Be coherent (4,5)
12 Small particle of a substance (7)
13 Thick-___ : insensitive to criticism (7)
14 Unfastened (6)
16 Mark ___ : Star Wars actor (6)
18 Yellow-green colour; small fruit (5)

CROSSWORD

No. 123

Across

1 Assent or agree to (6)
7 Consecrate (8)
8 Muhammad ___ : boxer (3)
9 Choose (6)
10 A hole that lets liquid escape (4)
11 Valuable thing or person (5)
13 Hot water spouts (7)
15 Planned one's actions (7)
17 Stage whisper (5)
21 Sailing ship (4)
22 Inclined at an angle (6)
23 Midge ___ : Ultravox musician (3)
24 Express as a number (8)
25 Put an end to (6)

Down

1 Type of rhododendron (6)
2 Serious situation (6)
3 Trees (anag) (5)
4 One more (7)
5 Designers of trendy clothes (8)
6 Matter (6)
12 Coming out of (8)
14 ___ Potter: English author (7)
16 Travelling show with clowns (6)
18 Admit to a post (6)
19 Entangle (6)
20 Cunning plans (5)

No. 124

Across

7 Line that bounds a circle (13)
8 Breakfast food (8)
9 Ends (4)
10 Scowled (7)
12 Move on ice (5)
14 Thaws (5)
16 Set aside for a purpose (7)
19 Flutter (4)
20 Reprove (8)
22 Shape or arrangement (13)

Down

1 Robert De ___ : actor (4)
2 Rare (6)
3 Very small amount (7)
4 Gave up; surrendered (5)
5 Comment (6)
6 Curved sword (8)
11 Fail to notice (8)
13 Agriculturalists (7)
15 Exemplify (6)
17 Sixty seconds (6)
18 Suspends (5)
21 Display (4)

CROSSWORD

No. 125

Across

1 Envy (8)
5 Killer whale (4)
9 No longer fresh (of food) (5)
10 Very masculine (5)
11 Made easier (10)
14 Surrenders (6)
15 Within this context (6)
17 Reduce speed (10)
20 Expect; think that (5)
21 Exceed; perform better than (5)
22 Pitcher (4)
23 Portents (8)

Down

1 Tease (4)
2 Unfortunately (4)
3 Ate excessively (12)
4 Angel of the highest order (6)
6 Accepted (8)
7 Evading (8)
8 Able to use both hands well (12)
12 Group of symptoms which occur together (8)
13 Creative (anag) (8)
16 ___ Conan Doyle: author (6)
18 Male deer (4)
19 Oodles (4)

No. 126

Across

1 Large periods of time (4)
3 Come nearer to (8)
9 Kettledrums (7)
10 Stinky (5)
11 Extremely large (12)
13 Softwood tree (6)
15 Lower someone's dignity (6)
17 Study of the properties of moving air (12)
20 Christina ___ : Addams Family actress (5)
21 Young chicken (7)
22 Move out the way of (8)
23 First man (4)

Down

1 Measure of the heat content of a system (8)
2 Confess to (5)
4 Toxin (6)
5 Cooling device (12)
6 Motivate (7)
7 Conceal (4)
8 Scientific research rooms (12)
12 Very small unit of length (8)
14 Penetrated (7)
16 Farewell remark (3-3)
18 Ticked over (of an engine) (5)
19 Part of the eye (4)

CROSSWORD

No. 127

Across

7 Protective covering (6)
8 Bronzed (6)
9 Arthur ___ : former US tennis player (4)
10 Large rigid dirigible (8)
11 Cheat; con (7)
13 High lending practice (5)
15 Uproarious party or fight (5)
16 Alan ___ : England footballer (7)
18 Top quality (of a hotel) (4-4)
19 Cameron ___ : actress (4)
21 Rough and uneven (of a cliff) (6)
22 Outer part of a bird's wing (6)

Down

1 Spheres (4)
2 Prescience (13)
3 Make mentally fatigued (7)
4 Paces (5)
5 Comprehension (13)
6 Pure-bred (of an animal) (8)
12 Fighters (8)
14 Type of treatment for a disorder (7)
17 Remains (5)
20 River of central England (4)

No. 128

Across

1 Person highly skilled in music (8)
5 Capital of the Ukraine (4)
8 Rounded mass (5)
9 Old-fashioned (7)
10 Vary the pitch of the voice (7)
12 Type of respiration (7)
14 Wealthy businessperson (7)
16 Eg Tuesday (7)
18 Bring a law into effect again (2-5)
19 Come into direct contact with (5)
20 Small pointed missile (4)
21 Plant with decorative leaves (8)

Down

1 Upper front part of a boot (4)
2 Computer networking device (6)
3 Not questioned by anyone (9)
4 Not moving (6)
6 Pictures (6)
7 Grammatical case in Latin (8)
11 Lost from memory (9)
12 Responded (8)
13 Extraterrestrial rock (6)
14 Believer in the occult (6)
15 Surprise attack (6)
17 Reasons; explanations (4)

CROSSWORD

No. 129

Across

1 Route (4)
3 Busy and active (8)
9 Have as a part (7)
10 Strong cords (5)
11 Consume a meal (3)
12 Tree of the birch family with toothed leaves (5)
13 Pipes (5)
15 Produce eggs (5)
17 Individual things (5)
18 23rd Greek letter (3)
19 Mark ___ : Samuel Langhorne Clemens (5)
20 Oval shape (7)
21 Sergeant (anag) (8)
22 Salver (4)

Down

1 Head of the government (5,8)
2 Implied (5)
4 Winged child (6)
5 Not guided by good sense (12)
6 Hindered (7)
7 Devastatingly (13)
8 Most perfect example of a quality (12)
14 Japanese flower arranging (7)
16 Fervent (6)
18 A written document (5)

No. 130

Across

1 Come before in time (8)
5 List of food items available (4)
9 Be the same as (5)
10 Raise up (5)
11 Fast food items (10)
14 Sum of money demanded to release a captive (6)
15 Aim to achieve something (6)
17 Appeal (10)
20 Game of chance (5)
21 Lukewarm (5)
22 Sight organs (4)
23 Be envious of (8)

Down

1 The highest point (4)
2 Tense (4)
3 Fellow plotter (12)
4 River in Europe (6)
6 Large outbreak of a disease (8)
7 Unproven (8)
8 Marksman (12)
12 Introduction (8)
13 Example (8)
16 Way of standing; posture (6)
18 Imitated (4)
19 Verge (4)

CROSSWORD

No. 131

Across

1 Indolent (4)
3 Form of government (8)
9 Light shoes (7)
10 Stage play (5)
11 The ___ Gatsby: F. Scott Fitzgerald novel (5)
12 Perfect happiness (7)
13 Arch of the foot (6)
15 Consider to be true (6)
17 Provider of financial cover (7)
18 Become subject to (5)
20 Word of farewell (5)
21 Concern; implicate (7)
22 Unable to discern musical pitch (4-4)
23 Sues (anag) (4)

Down

1 Petty (13)
2 ___ Armstrong: famous cyclist (5)
4 Relaxing (6)
5 Perform below expectation (12)
6 Discharge from a hole in a pipe (7)
7 Dull and uninteresting (13)
8 Place of conflict (12)
14 Official sitting (7)
16 Russian carriage (6)
19 Telephones (5)

No. 132

Across

1 Implement used for cleaning (5)
4 Acted properly (7)
7 Daniel ___ : James Bond actor (5)
8 Working dough (8)
9 Civilian dress (5)
11 Raised (8)
15 Hard shell of a crustacean (8)
17 Firearm (5)
19 Metallic element used in light bulbs (8)
20 Island in the Mediterranean Sea (5)
21 US state (7)
22 Sullen or moody (5)

Down

1 Apiarist (9)
2 Expressed audibly (7)
3 Tribal leader (7)
4 Copper and tin alloy (6)
5 Entrance hall (6)
6 Be alive; be real (5)
10 Security against a loss (9)
12 Cattle troughs (7)
13 Pertaining to actuality (7)
14 Part of a school uniform (6)
16 Former female pupil (6)
18 Suffuse with colour (5)

CROSSWORD

No. 133

Across

1 Attack with severe criticism (6)
4 Arachnid (6)
9 Spiny egg-laying mammal (7)
10 Prehistoric person (7)
11 Doglike mammal (5)
12 Capital of Bulgaria (5)
14 Cook meat in the oven (5)
15 Prod with the elbow (5)
17 Ditches (5)
18 Cocktail with gin and vermouth (7)
20 Took small bites out of (7)
21 Hearts (anag) (6)
22 Leave a place (6)

Down

1 Bubble violently (6)
2 Accomplished (8)
3 Monster with nine heads (5)
5 University official (7)
6 Small drink of spirits (4)
7 Country in central Africa (6)
8 Travelling with a rucksack (11)
13 Mathematical statements (8)
14 Revival (7)
15 Agile (6)
16 Incidental remarks (6)
17 Remove errors from software (5)
19 Hind part (4)

CROSSWORD

No. 134

Across

1 Device for inflating tyres (4)
3 Exhibitionists (4-4)
9 The exposure of bedrock (7)
10 Egg-shaped (5)
11 Jail term without end (4,8)
13 Money received (6)
15 Person to whom a lease is granted (6)
17 DIY stands for this (2-2-8)
20 ___ acid: protein building block (5)
21 Organic solvent (7)
22 International waters (4,4)
23 ___ Ifans: Welsh actor (4)

Down

1 Announce publicly (8)
2 Distinctive design (5)
4 Wishing for (6)
5 Showing complete commitment (12)
6 Debacles (7)
7 Grain (4)
8 Excessively forward (12)
12 Pamphlets (8)
14 Shutting (7)
16 Instrumental piece of music (6)
18 Period of time in history (5)
19 Sham (anag) (4)

SOLUTIONS

No. 1

P	O	U	N	D	S			L		P	R	Y
	P			E		I	R	I	S	H		A
E	P	S	I	L	O	N		S		A		R
	R			U		A		P	L	E	A	D
R	E	S	I	D	I	N	G			T		A
	S			I		E		E		O		G
I	S	L	A	N	D		G	L	A	N	C	E
G		O		G		C		E			L	
N		N			C	L	E	M	A	T	I	S
I	N	G	O	T		E		E			M	
T		E		O		A	N	N	U	L	A	R
E		S	A	F	E	R		T			T	
S	I	T		U			I	S	S	U	E	S

No. 2

	K		A		A		R		P		V	
U	N	A	D	U	L	T	E	R	A	T	E	D
	O		H		L		P		T		N	
E	T	H	E	R	E	A	L		E	D	G	Y
			R		G		Y		N		E	
S	T	E	E	P	E	D		S	T	U	F	F
	A				D		T				U	
O	X	L	I	P		R	E	C	O	I	L	S
	O		N		T		R		R			
I	N	K	S		H	A	R	D	B	A	C	K
	O		O		E		A		I		O	
A	M	P	L	I	F	I	C	A	T	I	O	N
	Y		E		T		E		S		S	

No. 3

D	E	L	E	G	A	T	E		L	E	I	A
R		I		A		U				T		S
O	F	F	E	R		N	O	U	G	H	T	S
P		T		D		D				A		E
		E		E		R	E	T	I	N	A	S
A	D	D	E	N	D	A		H		E		S
V				E				R				E
E		T		R		T	R	E	M	O	R	S
R	E	I	S	S	U	E		A		P		
S		N				R		T		I		B
I	N	S	U	L	A	R		E	R	N	I	E
O		E				O		N		E		A
N	U	L	L		C	R	U	S	A	D	E	R

No. 4

R	A	C	E		V	E	R	B	A	T	I	M
E		L		V		D		I		O		O
S	P	I	C	I	N	G		O	B	A	M	A
I		M		C		I		D		S		N
S	U	B	S	T	A	N	T	I	A	T	E	
T				O		G		V		E		H
O	C	C	U	R	S		D	E	C	R	E	E
R		O		I		A		R				P
	I	N	C	O	N	S	I	S	T	E	N	T
M		D		U		S		I		L		A
O	V	E	R	S		U	N	T	Y	I	N	G
T		M		L		R		Y		T		O
H	O	N	E	Y	D	E	W		A	E	O	N

No. 5

C	A	P	S	I	C	U	M		F	R	E	E
O		O		N		R		D		E		G
T	R	U	S	T		G		I	M	P	L	Y
S		T		E		E		S		R		P
			T	R	A	N	S	C	R	I	P	T
B		M		M		T		O		S		I
A	C	E	T	I	C		E	R	R	A	T	A
T		D		N		H		D		L		N
T	R	I	L	A	T	E	R	A	L			
E		E		B		A		N		Y		I
N	O	V	E	L		T		T	R	O	U	T
E		A		E		E		L		G		C
D	A	L	E		C	R	A	Y	F	I	S	H

No. 6

H	U	N	G		A	F	F	L	I	C	T	S
A		O		C		L		E		L		E
R	E	W	R	O	T	E		G	R	A	C	E
D		I		O		D		I		M		S
C	O	N	G	R	E	G	A	T	I	O	N	
O				D		E		I		U		P
P	R	E	F	I	X		A	M	O	R	A	L
Y		N		N		I		A				A
	S	T	R	A	I	G	H	T	A	W	A	Y
A		R		T		N		E		I		R
Q	U	A	S	I		O	R	L	A	N	D	O
U		N		O		R		Y		C		O
A	T	T	E	N	D	E	D		R	E	A	M

SOLUTIONS

No. 7

C		A		R				I		G		S
L	O	C	K	E	T		I	N	S	E	R	T
I		C		C		M		S		T		E
P	R	O	D	U	C	E		I	N	U	R	E
P		S		R		L		D		P		L
E	A	T	S		A	B	B	E	Y			
R		S		K		O		S		B		H
			E	N	N	U	I		F	E	T	A
H		C		O		R		U		W		M
I	N	L	A	W		N	A	N	N	I	E	S
G		A		H		E		D		T		T
H	A	R	R	O	W		M	I	S	C	U	E
S		E		W				D		H		R

No. 8

	D		A		C		T		S		M	
C	R	Y	P	T	O	G	R	A	P	H	E	R
	U		R		D		A		I		S	
E	M	P	O	R	I	U	M		N	E	S	T
			N		C		P		A		A	
T	O	P	S	P	I	N		F	L	A	G	S
	M				L		C				E	
K	N	E	A	D		C	L	O	S	E	S	T
	I		F		T		E		T			
E	V	I	L		A	N	A	C	O	N	D	A
	O		A		U		R		D		E	
C	R	I	M	I	N	O	L	O	G	I	S	T
	E		E		T		Y		Y		K	

No. 9

A		B		P				G		D		L
M	A	I	N	L	Y		B	R	E	E	Z	E
A		O		I		H		A		C		A
Z	A	M	B	E	Z	I		N	O	O	K	S
I		A		D		E		I		R		E
N	O	S	Y		C	R	A	T	E			
G		S		H		A		E		G		P
			L	A	I	R	D		H	U	L	L
C		K		L		C		A		S		A
H	A	I	T	I		H	A	U	G	H	T	Y
A		L		B		Y		R		I		I
S	I	N	F	U	L		C	A	N	N	O	N
E		S		T				L		G		G

No. 10

	Q	U	A	N	T	U	M	L	E	A	P	
E		T		A		R		U		R		G
X		I		I	S	A	A	C		S	I	R
P	A	L	E	R		N		I		O		A
E		I		O		U		D	E	N	I	M
D	A	T	A	B	A	S	E					O
I		Y		I				F		T		P
T					F	L	O	U	R	I	S	H
I	N	L	E	T		O		R		G		O
O		A		I		U		L	O	H	A	N
U	R	N		B	O	N	G	O		T		E
S		E		I		G		N		E		S
	E	S	T	A	T	E	A	G	E	N	T	

No. 11

C	O	U	P	E		U	P	H	O	L	D	S
O		S		N		N			R		A	
R		E		R		S		P	A	D	R	E
R	O	L	L	O	V	E	R		L		T	
E		E		B		E		F	L	E	S	H
C	I	S	T	E	R	N	S		Y			A
T		S		D				C		C		V
E			N		M	A	R	R	I	A	G	E
D	U	K	E	S		L		U		L		R
	M		A		E	P	I	S	O	D	E	S
A	B	E	T	S		A		H		E		A
	E		E			C		E		R		C
G	R	A	N	D	M	A		D	R	A	N	K

No. 12

E	E	L	S		O	P	T	I	M	I	S	M
X		I		C		O		M		L		E
P	O	L	A	R	I	S		P	I	L	E	D
A		A		O		T		E		N		I
N	E	C	K	S		E	A	R	N	E	S	T
S				S		D		S		S		E
I	N	S	E	C	T		D	O	W	S	E	R
V		T		O		R		N				R
E	V	A	C	U	E	E		A	C	C	R	A
N		G		N		M		T		O		N
E	I	G	H	T		A	N	O	D	Y	N	E
S		E		R		I		R		L		A
S	P	R	A	Y	I	N	G		R	Y	A	N

SOLUTIONS

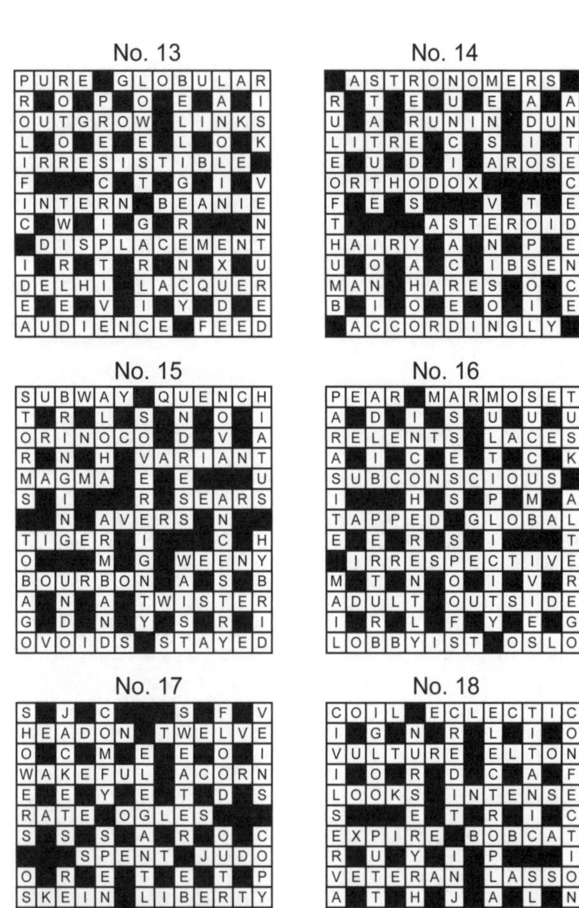

SOLUTIONS

No. 19

O	S	P	R	E	Y		A	S	L	E	E	P
C		A		P		P		E		L		R
C	A	S	H	I	E	R		V		L		I
U		T		C		E	M	E	R	A	L	D
P	A	R	I	S		C		R				E
Y		A				I		A	R	I	E	S
		M		L	A	P	E	L		D		
H	E	I	D	I		I				E		F
E				T		T		T	A	N	G	O
A	R	T	D	E	C	O		R		T		D
T		E		R		U	N	I	F	I	E	D
E		N		A		S		E		T		E
R	I	D	D	L	E		P	R	A	Y	E	R

No. 20

D	R	N	O		D	I	C	A	P	R	I	O
I		U		C		N		L		E		V
S	I	R	L	O	I	N		P	L	A	N	E
C		S		N		A		H		C		R
R	E	E	D	S		T	E	A	C	H	E	S
E				T		E		N		E		T
D	E	V	O	I	D		R	U	S	S	I	A
I		A		T		U		M				T
T	I	S	S	U	E	S		E	N	S	U	E
A		S		E		H		R		E		M
B	R	A	I	N		E	P	I	S	T	L	E
L		L		C		R		C		U		N
E	S	S	A	Y	I	S	T		S	P	A	T

No. 21

	S		P		P		H		A		E	
M	A	L	I	C	I	O	U	S	N	E	S	S
	R		M		A		T		C		S	
H	I	S	P	A	N	I	C		H	E	E	D
			L		O		H		O		N	
C	H	I	E	F	L	Y		B	R	U	C	E
	A				A		R				E	
A	N	D	R	E		N	E	W	N	E	S	S
	D		E		C		D		O			
I	S	L	A		E	C	O	N	O	M	I	C
	O		S		A		U		D		N	
I	M	P	O	S	S	I	B	I	L	I	T	Y
	E		N		E		T		E		O	

No. 22

S	T	E	E	R	S			Z		A	G	A
	R			E		S	W	I	M	S		B
T	U	N	I	S	I	A		N		P		O
	F			C		I		C	H	I	L	L
E	F	F	L	U	E	N	T			R		I
	L			I		T		F		I		S
L	E	A	R	N	S		H	A	U	N	C	H
U		B		G		E		R			L	
C		S			E	J	E	C	T	I	O	N
K	I	T	E	S		E		I			S	
I		A		E		C	A	C	K	L	E	S
L		I	N	E	R	T		A			U	
Y	E	N		P			S	L	U	M	P	S

No. 23

F	E	D	O	R	A		A		E		P	
U		E			G	A	M	B	L	E	R	S
G	A	S			A		E		E		O	
U		P	R	O	T	O	N		C	A	P	E
E		O			E		I		T		E	
S	I	T	U	P		S	T	E	R	I	L	E
			N		R		Y		I			
K	N	I	T	T	E	R		S	C	O	N	E
	E		I		D		O			R		X
S	C	A	M		T	O	P	P	E	D		U
	T		E		A		E			E	E	L
T	A	I	L	S	P	I	N			A		T
	R		Y		E		S	H	E	L	L	S

No. 24

	S	C	I	N	T	I	L	L	A	T	E	
E		A		U		N		O		A		S
M		S		A	T	L	A	S		B	O	O
B	A	C	O	N		A		E		O		L
A		A		C		N		S	T	O	M	A
R	E	D	H	E	A	D	S					R
R		E		S				J		H		S
A					A	S	T	U	T	E	L	Y
S	I	S	A	L		A		J		L		S
S		I		I		L		I	N	P	U	T
E	G	G		M	E	A	N	T		F		E
D		H		B		M		S		U		M
	A	T	R	O	C	I	O	U	S	L	Y	

SOLUTIONS

No. 25

A	P	L	O	M	B		D	A	W	D	L	E
L		I		A		C		N		A		N
I	N	F	E	R	N	O		O		U		T
G		E		I		N	A	M	I	B	I	A
H	A	L	T	S		F		A				I
T		E				O		L	O	C	A	L
		S		S	A	U	C	Y		A		
B	A	S	I	C		N				R		C
U				H		D		O	D	O	U	R
M	A	R	C	O	N	I		U		U		E
B		H		O		N	A	T	A	S	H	A
L		E		L		G		E		E		M
E	L	A	P	S	E		T	R	I	L	B	Y

No. 26

R	U	S	E		D	A	N	D	R	U	F	F
E		H		O		R		I		P		L
M	A	R	I	L	Y	N		S	U	S	H	I
O		U		D		O		I		W		R
R	O	B	O	T		L	E	N	I	E	N	T
S				E		D		F		P		A
E	M	B	O	S	S		S	E	P	T	E	T
L		O		T		S		C				I
E	X	T	R	A	C	T		T	O	K	Y	O
S		A		M		O		I		O		U
S	E	N	S	E		L	O	O	F	A	H	S
L		I		N		E		N		L		L
Y	A	C	H	T	I	N	G		N	A	V	Y

No. 27

B	E	M	U	S	E		D		U		H	
O		A			G	U	E	R	N	S	E	Y
D	E	N			Y		P		L		C	
E		T	I	P	P	L	E		A	C	T	S
G		R			T		N		W		I	
A	L	A	R	M		E	D	I	F	I	C	E
			H		K		S		U			
P	L	A	Y	P	E	N		C	L	I	F	F
	A		T		E		S			N		O
A	R	C	H		P	I	C	N	I	C		R
	V		M		I		R			U	S	A
P	A	T	I	E	N	C	E			R		G
	L		C		G		W	R	A	S	S	E

No. 28

D	A	H	L		D	A	Y	D	R	E	A	M
O		E		S		L		E		N		I
W	A	L	K	E	R	S		M	I	L	L	S
N		E		L		A		O		I		C
I	N	N		F		C		N	O	V	A	E
N				L	E	E	R	S		E		L
G		S		E				T		N		L
S		T		S	O	B	E	R				A
T	R	I	M	S		I		A		B	I	N
R		R		N		G		B		Y		E
E	E	R	I	E		G	A	L	I	L	E	O
E		U		S		E		E		A		U
T	A	P	E	S	T	R	Y		E	W	E	S

No. 29

D	E	S	I	R	E		H	U	R	L	E	D
E		R		A		S		T		U		I
F	R	I	Z	Z	L	E		T		L		E
E		L		O		T	R	E	L	L	I	S
C	H	A	I	R		T		R				E
T		N				L		L	O	Y	A	L
		K		B	E	E	F	Y		I		
T	I	A	R	A		M				E		B
A				R		E		C	E	L	L	O
N	E	U	T	R	O	N		U		D		L
D		P		I		T	O	P	S	I	D	E
E		O		N		S		I		N		R
M	A	N	A	G	E		A	D	A	G	I	O

No. 30

	C	O	N	N	O	T	A	T	I	O	N	
W		S		U		H		O		U		S
E		S		C	H	E	E	P		N	E	T
S	W	I	L	L		S		I		C		A
T		C		E		I		C	L	E	G	G
C	O	L	L	A	P	S	E					E
O		E		R				O		B		F
U					W	A	Y	F	A	R	E	R
N	I	N	T	H		T		F		A		I
T		A		O		T		S	T	I	N	G
R	O	D		K	H	A	K	I		L		H
Y		A		U		I		D		L		T
	I	L	L	M	A	N	N	E	R	E	D	

SOLUTIONS

No. 31

	D	I	S	G	R	A	C	E	F	U	L	
R		M		O		V		A		S		P
E		P		S	W	I	N	G		A	I	L
S	Y	L	P	H		D		L		G		A
U		O		A		L		E	L	E	G	Y
S	I	D	E	W	A	Y	S					O
C		E		K				V		E		N
I					C	O	L	E	S	L	A	W
T	U	F	T	S		R		R		I		O
A		I		W		G		M	E	T	E	R
T	U	N		A	B	A	T	E		I		D
E		E		S		N		E		S		S
	O	R	C	H	E	S	T	R	A	T	E	

No. 32

S	C	R	I	B	E			M		A	W	L
	A			O		A	V	E	R	T		I
S	T	A	T	U	E	S		S		T		B
	C			Q		P		S	T	A	T	E
C	H	E	R	U	B	I	C			C		R
	U			E		C		D		H		A
S	P	O	T	T	Y		C	E	R	E	A	L
E		P		S		M		L			S	
N		E			N	A	M	E	S	A	K	E
E	A	R	E	D		T		T			A	
G		A		U		E	X	I	G	E	N	T
A		N	I	P	P	Y		O			C	
L	A	D		E			E	N	T	R	E	E

No. 33

A	T	T	E	S	T		G		E		U	
B		A			W	O	R	R	Y	I	N	G
S	I	T			I		I		E		I	
O		T	U	R	N	I	P		B	U	S	T
R		O			S		P		R		O	
B	L	O	B	S		R	E	D	O	I	N	G
			U		C		D		W			
A	E	O	L	I	A	N		A	S	L	A	N
	X		K		R		S			O		E
E	T	C	H		R	E	T	I	N	A		A
	R		E		I		R			T	O	R
J	A	L	A	P	E	N	O			H		B
	S		D		D		P	U	R	E	L	Y

No. 34

S	T	R	E	S	S			S		C	O	O
	A			U		I	N	T	E	R		U
D	I	V	I	D	E	S		U		A		T
	L			D		S		N	O	M	A	D
W	O	R	K	E	D	U	P			P		O
	R			N		E		F		E		E
U	S	A	B	L	E		H	O	R	D	E	S
N		I		Y		W		U			S	
H		R			S	H	E	R	L	O	C	K
A	S	S	A	Y		I		T			A	
P		H		U		P	R	E	C	E	P	T
P		O	V	A	L	S		E			E	
Y	E	W		N			U	N	T	I	D	Y

No. 35

M	O	N	S	T	E	R	S		G	N	A	W
I		I		U		O				E		I
S	I	T	A	R		B	A	R	B	E	L	L
S		W		B		B				S		D
		I		U		E	A	S	E	O	F	F
B	A	T	T	L	E	R		T		N		I
L				E				R				R
U		F		N		G	R	E	N	A	D	E
B	R	I	S	T	L	Y		T		F		
B		S				P		C		R		F
E	S	C	A	P	E	S		H	A	I	K	U
R		A				U		E		C		R
Y	O	L	K		E	M	I	S	S	A	R	Y

No. 36

	B		C		G		S		P		P	
J	A	G	U	A	R		P	L	A	N	A	R
	K		T		U		I		R		R	
D	U	S	T		B	E	T	R	A	Y	A	L
			H		B		E		P		L	
S	C	H	E	M	E	S		W	H	I	L	E
	R		M		D		D		E		E	
S	I	N	U	S		M	I	S	R	U	L	E
	T		S		A		P		N			
M	I	R	T	H	F	U	L		A	L	O	E
	Q		A		O		O		L		V	
Q	U	A	R	T	O		M	A	I	L	E	D
	E		D		T		A		A		N	

SOLUTIONS

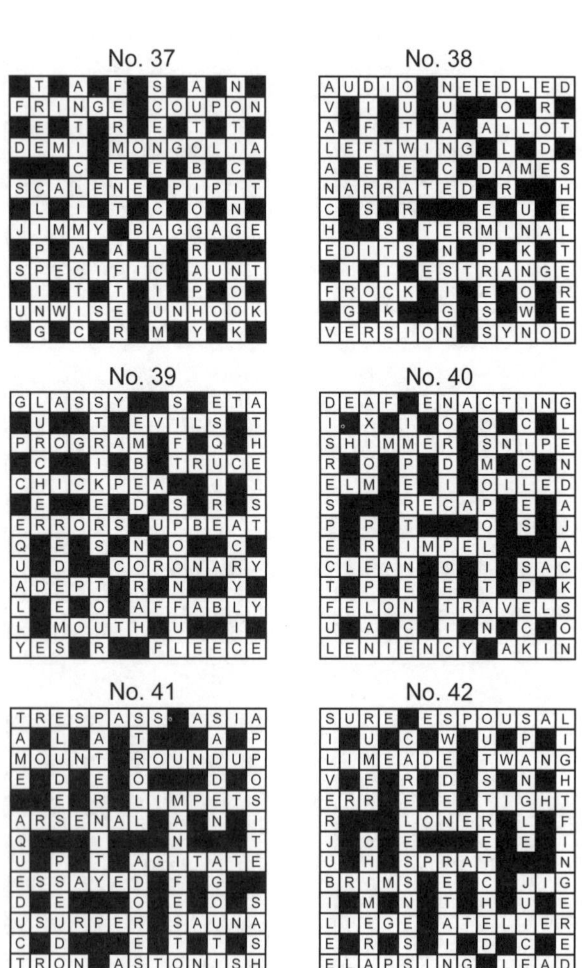

No. 43

S	I	L	E	N	T		S	T	A	G	E	D
I		U		I		H		I		R		A
L	A	S	A	G	N	E		D		A		I
I		C		E		A	V	I	G	N	O	N
C	R	I	E	R		D		N				T
A		O				T		G	U	L	L	Y
		U		P	O	E	T	S		O		
B	A	S	I	L		A				N		P
I				U		C		R	E	G	A	L
S	C	R	U	N	C	H		E		H		A
H		U		D		E	C	S	T	A	S	Y
O		B		E		R		T		U		E
P	A	S	T	R	Y		O	S	T	L	E	R

No. 44

A	T	H	L	E	T	I	C		H	U	F	F
N		A		N		N				N		R
T	U	R	N	S		S	I	R	O	C	C	O
E		D		H		A				L		N
		L		R		N	E	A	R	E	S	T
S	K	Y	L	I	N	E		T		S		I
Q				N				T				E
U		S		E		F	R	E	E	Z	E	R
I	N	C	I	S	O	R		N		A		
R		R				E		U		M		N
R	O	U	G	H	E	N		A	M	B	L	E
E		F				Z		T		I		A
L	I	F	E		T	Y	P	E	C	A	S	T

No. 45

M	O	B	S		C	U	S	H	I	O	N	S
I		U		C		N		O		U		U
S	U	I	T	O	R	S		P	U	T	T	S
C		L		M		U		E		C		A
H	U	T		M		R		L	E	A	R	N
I				O	B	E	S	E		S		S
E		T		N				S		T		A
V		H		W	A	G	E	S				R
O	Z	O	N	E		A		N		S	E	A
U		R		A		T		E		M		N
S	P	E	L	L		E	A	S	T	E	N	D
L		A		T		A		S		L		O
Y	O	U	T	H	F	U	L		F	L	A	N

No. 46

L	O	L	L	I	P	O	P		G	R	U	B
E		E		N		U		S		E		A
S	W	E	A	T		N		T	R	A	W	L
T		R		E		C		R		L		D
			A	L	L	E	G	A	T	I	O	N
S		G		L		S		I		S		E
P	E	R	M	I	T		A	G	R	E	E	S
E		E		G		N		H		S		S
C	O	N	T	I	N	U	I	T	Y			
I		A		B		C		E		O		G
M	E	D	A	L		L		N	A	N	N	Y
E		E		Y		E		E		C		M
N	A	S	H		M	I	N	D	L	E	S	S

No. 47

C	E	I	L	I	N	G	S		A	D	D	S
H		D		N		A				R		I
E	R	E	C	T		L	A	N	T	E	R	N
R		A		E		L				D		I
		L		N		O	B	L	I	G	E	S
D	E	S	K	T	O	P		E		E		T
R				I				G				E
A		G		O		S	L	I	T	H	E	R
G	R	O	W	N	U	P		O		A		
O		P				R		N		V		J
O	P	H	E	L	I	A		A	M	A	Z	E
N		E				W		R		N		R
S	E	R	F		P	L	A	Y	B	A	C	K

No. 48

A	B	H	O	R		A	L	R	E	A	D	Y
N		E		O		G			X		E	
A		R		U		A		H	U	B	B	Y
E	V	E	N	N	E	S	S		D		T	
R		T		D		S		D	E	N	S	E
O	L	I	V	E	O	I	L			S		X
B		C		R				S		D		C
I			W		C	O	M	P	R	I	S	E
C	R	E	E	K		D		E		V		S
	E		A		B	I	S	C	U	I	T	S
E	V	O	K	E		O		T		N		I
	U		E			U		R		E		V
R	E	G	R	E	S	S		A	G	R	E	E

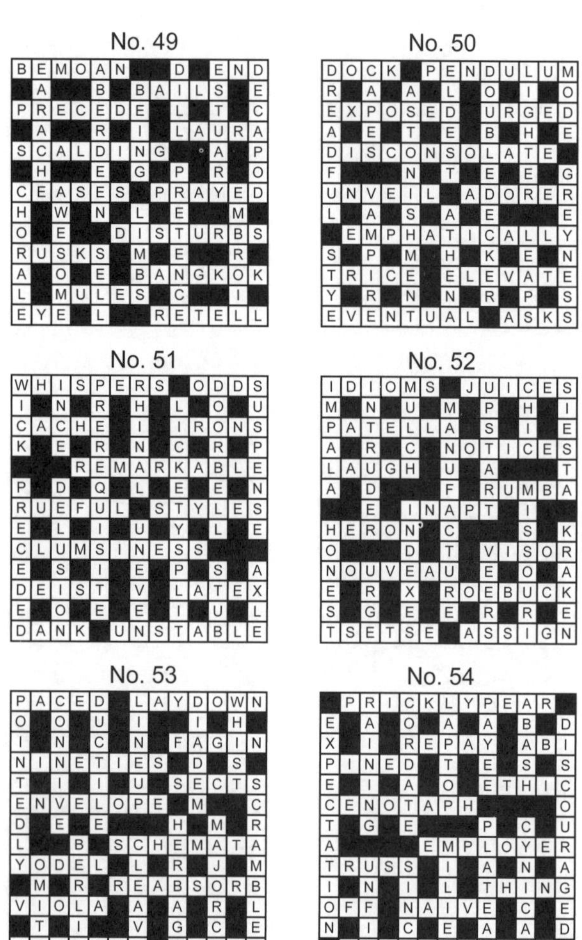
No. 49
No. 50
No. 51
No. 52
No. 53
No. 54

No. 55

M	O	D	E	M		E	N	D	E	M	I	C
A		I		E		A			U		N	
L		S		S		T		C	R	E	D	O
I	N	G	E	S	T	E	D		O		I	
G		U		A		R		S	P	L	A	T
N	O	S	E	G	A	Y	S		E			R
A		T		E				A		P		U
N			L		C	U	L	D	E	S	A	C
T	O	P	A	Z		N		O		Y		U
	N		M		C	L	E	R	I	C	A	L
A	S	K	E	D		I		N		H		E
	E		N			K		E		I		N
S	T	A	T	U	R	E		D	U	C	A	T

No. 56

F	I	B	U	L	A		A	B	A	T	E	D
A		A		A		C		R		A		E
M	I	L	I	T	I	A		E		X		F
I		L		T		L	O	W	R	I	S	E
S	T	Y	L	E		C		E				A
H		H				U		R	I	G	H	T
		O		I	N	L	A	Y		L		
F	R	O	W	N		A				E		B
A				E		T		I	M	A	G	O
S	A	M	U	R	A	I		D		M		N
C		A		T		O	B	E	Y	I	N	G
I		N		I		N		A		N		O
A	N	Y	W	A	Y		A	L	I	G	N	S

No. 57

S	I	D	E		G	A	L	A	C	T	I	C
I		R		S		R		R		O		L
G	L	O	B	U	L	E		C	A	P	R	I
N		L		B		N		H		M		V
I	S	L	E	T		A	D	I	P	O	S	E
F				E		S		T		S		A
I	N	B	O	R	N		B	E	A	T	E	N
C		O		R		A		C				D
A	N	N	U	A	L	S		T	E	R	S	E
N		A		N		T		U		E		R
T	I	N	G	E		E	A	R	N	E	R	S
L		Z		A		R		E		V		O
Y	E	A	R	N	I	N	G		B	E	A	N

No. 58

B	O	W	S	P	R	I	T		S	P	U	D
A		E		R		C		A		R		E
R	E	T	R	O		O		L	O	O	S	E
S		S		F		N		L		V		P
			D	E	F	I	N	I	T	I	O	N
S		D		S		C		T		N		E
T	H	I	R	S	T		R	E	A	C	T	S
R		V		I		V		R		E		S
E	C	O	N	O	M	I	C	A	L			
A		R		N		R		T		S		H
M	O	C	H	A		A		I	N	T	R	O
E		E		L		G		O		A		O
R	E	D	O		C	O	R	N	E	R	E	D

No. 59

	T	E	M	P	E	S	T	U	O	U	S	
G		N		I		P		N		N		D
I		D		G	R	O	A	T		L	I	E
N	O	I	S	E		R		I		I		V
G		N		O		T		E	X	T	R	A
E	D	G	I	N	E	S	S					L
R		S		S				V		M		U
B					D	E	M	E	R	A	R	A
R	U	R	A	L		N		R		M		T
E		I		L		L		T	E	M	P	I
A	D	O		A	L	I	B	I		O		O
D		J		M		S		G		T		N
	C	A	T	A	S	T	R	O	P	H	E	

No. 60

R	E	S	I	S	T	E	D		B	L	O	C
O		P		T		X				O		O
L	A	Y	E	R		T	Y	P	I	C	A	L
L		I		A		E				A		O
		N		N		N	E	E	D	L	E	S
E	N	G	A	G	E	D		N		S		S
L				E				S				A
O		J		S		S	T	E	N	C	I	L
Q	U	A	R	T	E	T		M		O		
U		R				U		B		N		T
E	R	R	A	T	I	C		L	O	F	T	Y
N		E				C		E		E		P
T	I	D	Y		C	O	N	S	T	R	U	E

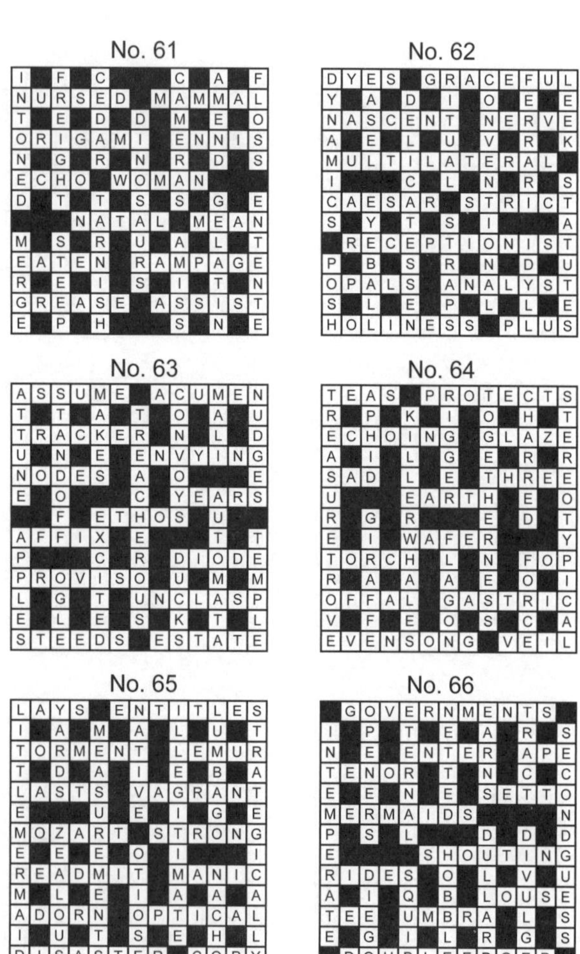
No. 61
No. 62
No. 63
No. 64
No. 65
No. 66

SOLUTIONS

No. 67

	S		D		U		A		A		R	
A	E	R	I	A	L		D	I	G	G	E	R
	A		S		Y		A		G		P	
W	R	I	T		S	U	P	P	L	I	E	R
			R		S		T		O		L	
P	R	E	E	N	E	D		S	M	E	L	T
	E		S		S		C		E		E	
C	A	U	S	E		C	O	M	R	A	D	E
	C		I		S		N		A			
P	H	O	N	E	T	I	C		T	A	M	P
	I		G		R		E		I		E	
A	N	G	L	I	A		P	R	O	B	E	D
	G		Y		W		T		N		K	

No. 68

S	T	R	A	D	D	L	E		E	B	B	S
I		O		I		A		U		E		A
C	L	A	M	S		R		N	O	L	I	N
K		D		I		V		B		I		C
			E	N	G	A	G	E	M	E	N	T
S		F		T		E		L		V		I
U	N	I	T	E	S		D	I	G	E	S	T
R		N		G		S		E		D		Y
F	I	G	U	R	A	T	I	V	E			
A		E		A		A		A		G		S
C	A	R	E	T		R		B	E	R	Y	L
E		E		E		E		L		I		A
D	A	D	S		A	D	D	E	N	D	U	M

No. 69

C	U	R	T		L	U	C	K	Y	D	I	P
O		O		I		N		A		E		R
N	O	M	I	N	E	E		L	U	C	R	E
S		A		C		A		E		A		T
C	A	N	T	O		S	P	I	N	D	L	E
I				M		Y		D		E		N
E	S	C	A	P	E		C	O	R	S	E	T
N		O		E		A		S				I
T	R	U	S	T	E	D		C	A	N	D	O
I		R		E		M		O		O		U
O	F	T	E	N		I	M	P	O	S	E	S
U		E		C		R		E		E		L
S	A	D	D	E	N	E	D		E	S	P	Y

No. 70

C	R	A	S	S		P	O	I	S	O	N	S
U		Z		C		R			C		O	
R		I		E		O		W	R	I	T	E
I	M	M	I	N	E	N	T		A		E	
O		U		E		T		S	P	A	D	E
U	L	T	E	R	I	O	R		S			R
S		H		Y				T		A		R
L			L		E	S	P	R	E	S	S	O
Y	O	K	E	S		T		O		C		N
	T		G		C	A	R	O	T	E	N	E
S	H	E	E	T		T		P		T		O
	E		N			U		E		I		U
E	R	U	D	I	T	E		D	O	C	K	S

No. 71

E	T	N	A		T	E	M	P	T	I	N	G
T		T		I		D		E		N		A
C	H	I	A	N	T	I		R	E	S	E	T
E		N		C		S		S		U		E
T	R	I	G	O	N	O	M	E	T	R	Y	
E				M		N		V		E		S
R	E	C	I	P	E		S	E	E	S	A	W
A		A		A		S		R				E
	A	P	P	R	E	C	I	A	T	I	V	E
A		T		A		A		N		C		P
C	R	U	M	B		M	A	C	H	I	N	E
H		R		L		P		E		L		R
E	X	E	G	E	S	I	S		B	Y	E	S

No. 72

E	S	T	E	E	M		G		E		C	
Q		R			I	L	L	U	S	O	R	Y
U	S	E			R		A		C		A	
I		B	A	N	T	A	M		A	L	T	O
N		L			H		O		R		E	
E	X	E	R	T		H	U	N	G	A	R	Y
			O		T		R		O			
P	R	A	Y	E	R	S		S	T	O	O	L
	E		A		I		E			N		O
I	D	O	L		R	E	V	I	E	W		O
	H		I		E		E			A	C	T
C	O	N	S	U	M	E	R			R		E
	T		T		E		Y	O	N	D	E	R

SOLUTIONS

No. 73

A	S	T	U	T	E		H	E	A	R	T	S
P		H		H		B		X		U		T
P	R	A	I	R	I	E		P		F		O
E		N		O		N	E	E	D	F	U	L
A	S	K	E	W		E		C				I
L		Y				V		T	R	I	E	D
		O		F	R	O	G	S		N		
S	A	U	D	I		L				F		R
I				G		E		S	M	I	L	E
S	O	L	O	M	O	N		M		N		N
T		O		E		C	H	A	L	I	C	E
E		O		N		E		R		T		W
R	O	T	A	T	E		O	T	H	E	R	S

No. 74

E		F		R				R		B		R
L	U	L	L	E	D		M	A	K	E	D	O
I		A		S		V		G		L		U
C	O	R	S	I	C	A		T	I	L	T	S
I		E		N		C		I		Y		E
T	H	U	S		S	C	A	M	P			
S		P		D		I		E		T		I
			A	R	E	N	A		E	A	R	N
S		M		I		A		S		L		G
W	H	I	F	F		T	H	I	C	K	E	R
E		N		T		E		L		I		E
P	E	E	R	E	D		S	K	U	N	K	S
T		R		D				Y		G		S

No. 75

U	N	C	O	R	K		A		S		A	
N		I			N	E	M	A	T	O	D	E
R	A	N			O		U		A		R	
E		E	X	A	C	T	S		C	O	O	T
A		M			K		I		C		I	
L	E	A	V	E		I	N	F	A	N	T	S
			I		P		G		T			
F	I	N	G	E	R	S		C	O	R	G	I
	N		O		E		B			E		M
A	V	E	R		V	I	O	L	A	S		P
	E		O		E		S			O	W	E
I	N	N	U	E	N	D	O			R		D
	T		S		T		N	E	T	T	L	E

No. 76

C	H	E	C	K	O	U	T		D	E	F	T
U		A		O		P				X		W
B	U	R	M	A		D	I	S	P	O	S	E
A		F		L		I				D		E
		U		A		K	I	B	B	U	T	Z
S	O	L	U	B	L	E		R		S		E
T				E				I				R
R		E		A		E	S	C	O	R	T	S
E	M	B	A	R	K	S		A		E		
S		B				C		B		M		L
S	H	I	A	T	S	U		R	O	O	M	Y
E		N				D		A		V		R
D	I	G	S		C	O	N	C	R	E	T	E

No. 77

S		O		U				F		P		L
U	R	S	I	N	E		K	O	R	U	N	A
B		T		P		T		R		P		R
V	U	L	P	I	N	E		F	L	A	N	K
E		E		N		S		E		E		S
R	A	R	E		A	T	T	I	C			
T		S		N		I		T		C		M
			R	E	E	F	S		I	O	T	A
A		L		S		I		E		U		R
C	R	A	F	T		E	N	G	I	N	E	S
T		P		L		S		G		S		H
O	U	S	T	E	D		P	E	S	E	T	A
R		E		D				D		L		L

No. 78

M	Y	T	H		A	B	S	O	L	U	T	E
A		H		N		U		B		N		F
G	U	I	T	A	R	S		S	C	A	R	F
N		E		R		H		C		I		E
I	N	F	E	R		E	C	U	A	D	O	R
F				O		L		R		E		V
I	N	L	A	W	S		C	A	N	D	L	E
C		I		M		H		N				S
A	C	Q	U	I	R	E		T	O	N	I	C
T		U		N		N		I		E		E
I	L	I	A	D		R	U	S	S	I	A	N
O		D		E		Y		M		G		C
N	O	S	E	D	I	V	E		S	H	O	E

SOLUTIONS

No. 79

U	N	F	O	L	D		A	F	F	R	A	Y
N		L		I		I		L		O		O
C	R	I	M	S	O	N		I		T		D
U		P		P		C	O	G	N	A	T	E
R	A	F	T	S		L		H				L
L		L				I		T	I	M	E	S
		O		A	N	N	O	Y		A		
P	O	P	U	P		A				C		E
O				R		T		E	T	H	E	R
T	E	R	M	I	N	I		X		I		O
T		O		O		O	P	P	O	S	E	D
E		A		R		N		E		M		E
D	O	M	A	I	N		F	L	O	O	D	S

No. 80

A	C	T	I	N	G		O		T		G	
V		R			E	M	P	H	A	S	I	S
E	M	U			E		T		S		A	
R		M	U	E	S	L	I		M	A	N	E
T		P			E		O		A		T	
S	I	S	Q	O		O	N	E	N	E	S	S
			U		P		S		I			
A	S	S	A	U	L	T		L	A	B	E	L
	T		G		A		G			E		A
B	A	L	M		T	H	R	O	N	G		R
	R		I		O		E			G	U	Y
E	V	E	R	Y	O	N	E			A		N
	E		E		N		T	H	O	R	A	X

No. 81

J		C		E				I		M		S
A	C	H	I	N	G		I	N	T	A	C	T
R		E		V		S		H		R		O
R	A	V	I	O	L	I		A	O	R	T	A
I		R		Y		G		L		Y		T
N	O	O	N		S	H	R	E	W			
G		N		B		T		D		B		T
			N	O	B	L	E		B	E	T	A
V		D		N		E		S		L		N
I	R	A	T	E		S	A	C	K	I	N	G
E		T		D		S		A		E		E
W	H	E	R	R	Y		E	L	E	V	E	N
S		S		Y				D		E		T

No. 82

C	O	O	K		T	R	A	M	W	A	Y	S
L		R		N		A		A		R		E
O	M	I	N	O	U	S		T	R	I	L	L
S		B		N		C		H		Z		F
E	V	I	T	A		A	N	E	M	O	N	E
D				L		L		M		N		V
C	O	E	R	C	E		S	A	F	A	R	I
I		Q		O		S		T				D
R	O	U	G	H	L	Y		I	M	A	G	E
C		A		O		L		C		Z		N
U	N	T	I	L		V	I	A	D	U	C	T
I		O		I		I		L		R		L
T	U	R	N	C	O	A	T		B	E	V	Y

No. 83

E	M	B	O	S	S	E	D		S	O	Y	A
B		I		T		D		U		P		S
O	L	D	E	R		I		N	A	I	L	S
R		S		A		C		A		N		I
			S	T	A	T	I	S	T	I	C	S
A		S		O		S		S		O		T
P	O	T	A	S	H		Q	U	I	N	C	E
P		R		P		B		M		S		D
A	P	O	T	H	E	O	S	I	S			
L		N		E		N		N		P		H
L	A	G	E	R		S		G	U	I	S	E
E		E		E		A		L		L		N
D	A	R	K		B	I	C	Y	C	L	E	S

No. 84

A	L	S	O		S	W	E	E	P	I	N	G
D		C		H		A		N		N		O
V	A	R	I	O	U	S		T	R	I	A	L
E		U		M		H		H		T		D
R	O	B		E		E		U	N	I	T	E
T				L	O	R	D	S		A		N
I		P		E				I		L		J
S		R		S	Y	R	I	A				U
E	V	E	N	S		A		S		D	A	B
M		L		N		P		T		A		I
E	L	U	D	E		P	A	I	N	F	U	L
N		D		S		E		C		F		E
T	R	E	A	S	U	R	Y		H	Y	P	E

SOLUTIONS

No. 85

M		E		A				R		T		T
O	B	S	E	S	S		D	E	L	E	T	E
S		P		T		I		S		X		N
E	G	O	T	I	S	M		H	E	A	P	S
L		U		R		B		A		S		E
L	O	S	S		C	R	E	P	E			
E		E		N		U		E		P		C
			W	E	I	G	H		T	R	I	O
B		S		T		L		S		U		N
E	X	C	E	L		I	N	T	O	N	E	S
E		R		I		A		I		I		I
P	R	A	N	K	S		B	L	A	N	K	S
S		M		E				T		G		T

No. 86

	M		S		S		E		C		R	
R	E	S	E	L	L		A	B	O	D	E	S
	A		V		I		R		U		A	
A	D	Z	E		M	I	L	D	N	E	S	S
			N		M		Y		T		O	
F	U	R	T	H	E	R		J	E	A	N	S
	N		H		R		P		R		E	
P	A	T	H	S		P	E	R	F	I	D	Y
	W		E		H		D		E			
P	A	R	A	B	O	L	A		I	N	C	H
	R		V		P		N		T		A	
R	E	C	E	D	E		T	H	E	F	T	S
	S		N		S		S		R		S	

No. 87

P	E	E	L		S	P	A	C	E	M	A	N
S		G		P		I		I		U		O
A	I	R	D	R	O	P		R	I	S	E	R
L		E		O		I		R		T		M
M	O	T	I	V	A	T	I	O	N	A	L	
I				I		S		C		N		B
S	T	A	N	D	S		K	U	N	G	F	U
T		M		E		S		M				T
	S	O	M	N	A	M	B	U	L	I	S	T
T		U		T		A		L		N		E
H	A	N	O	I		C	R	U	I	S	E	R
U		T		A		K		S		E		U
D	I	S	C	L	O	S	E		S	T	O	P

No. 88

	C	O	M	F	O	R	T	A	B	L	Y	
N		U		R		A		R		U		H
E		T		E	A	T	E	R		C	H	I
W	I	P	E	S		I		O		C		G
S		O		H		O		W	R	A	T	H
R	U	S	T	L	I	N	G					W
E		T		Y				S		A		A
A					A	M	I	C	A	B	L	Y
D	O	P	E	Y		A		E		D		C
E		O		A		D		P	H	O	T	O
R	A	W		R	E	M	I	T		M		D
S		E		N		A		I		E		E
	P	R	O	S	A	N	D	C	O	N	S	

No. 89

	L		H		O		T		S		A	
A	U	P	A	I	R		W	I	E	L	D	S
	G		L		E		I		L		H	
B	E	E	F		G	I	R	A	F	F	E	S
			H		A		L		C		S	
D	E	M	E	S	N	E		S	O	L	I	D
	M		A		O		O		N		V	
S	P	A	R	E		S	C	A	T	T	E	R
	H		T		G		U		A			
B	A	S	E	B	A	L	L		I	R	A	N
	T		D		R		I		N		W	
P	I	G	L	E	T		S	C	E	N	E	S
	C		Y		H		T		D		S	

No. 90

A		S		A				G		A		T
S	C	H	I	S	T		L	O	U	D	L	Y
T		I		C		A		S		D		S
O	F	F	L	O	A	D		S	A	L	V	O
U		T		T		D		I		E		N
N	E	E	D		G	R	I	P	E			
D		D		S		E		S		S		I
			G	O	O	S	E		E	T	O	N
S		B		B		S		S		A		T
T	H	R	O	B		E	M	P	E	R	O	R
A		I		I		E		I		L		U
S	I	D	I	N	G		U	N	B	E	N	D
H		E		G				S		T		E

SOLUTIONS

No. 91

P	E	N	D	A	N	T	S	■	S	C	U	T
A	■	I	■	P	■	A	■	■	■	O	■	R
C	O	M	M	A	■	S	C	A	P	U	L	A
E	■	B	■	T	■	S	■	■	■	N	■	N
■	■	U	■	H	■	E	X	C	I	T	E	S
R	U	S	S	E	L	L	■	U	■	Y	■	M
A	■	■	■	T	■	■	■	R	■	■	■	I
M	■	S	■	I	■	O	U	T	L	A	S	T
P	O	L	E	C	A	T	■	A	■	N	■	■
A	■	O	■	■	■	T	■	I	■	G	■	D
R	E	P	L	I	C	A	■	L	O	L	L	Y
T	■	E	■	■	■	W	■	E	■	E	■	E
S	O	S	O	■	W	A	N	D	E	R	E	D

No. 92

■	D	■	R	■	J	■	T	■	I	■	A	■
S	E	N	O	R	A	■	W	I	N	I	N	G
■	A	■	U	■	V	■	E	■	A	■	G	■
S	L	O	G	■	E	X	E	M	P	T	E	D
■	■	■	H	■	L	■	T	■	P	■	L	■
M	A	L	A	R	I	A	■	T	R	A	I	L
■	R	■	N	■	N	■	S	■	O	■	C	■
P	R	I	D	E	■	S	T	O	P	G	A	P
■	A	■	R	■	D	■	I	■	R	■	■	■
I	N	T	E	G	R	A	L	■	I	T	E	M
■	G	■	A	■	I	■	T	■	A	■	U	■
H	E	N	D	O	N	■	O	U	T	C	R	Y
■	D	■	Y	■	K	■	N	■	E	■	O	■

No. 93

T	I	C	K	■	S	T	A	I	R	W	A	Y
R	■	O	■	C	■	R	■	L	■	A	■	O
A	M	P	H	O	R	A	■	L	U	R	I	D
N	■	S	■	N	■	S	■	U	■	M	■	A
S	L	E	D	G	E	H	A	M	M	E	R	■
A	■	■	■	R	■	Y	■	I	■	S	■	S
C	O	L	L	A	R	■	S	N	A	T	C	H
T	■	I	■	T	■	E	■	A	■	■	■	A
■	M	A	N	U	F	A	C	T	U	R	E	D
E	■	I	■	L	■	R	■	I	■	E	■	O
P	A	S	T	A	■	W	O	O	D	R	O	W
I	■	O	■	T	■	I	■	N	■	U	■	E
C	O	N	V	E	R	G	E	■	E	N	I	D

No. 94

D	■	B	■	O	■	■	■	V	■	I	■	F
E	U	L	O	G	Y	■	M	I	D	D	L	E
S	■	A	■	R	■	O	■	S	■	L	■	A
P	A	R	V	E	N	U	■	I	D	E	A	S
A	■	I	■	S	■	T	■	O	■	R	■	T
I	N	N	S	■	U	S	I	N	G	■	■	■
R	■	G	■	B	■	K	■	S	■	I	■	S
■	■	■	B	E	G	I	N	■	E	M	I	T
T	■	P	■	D	■	R	■	A	■	P	■	R
S	C	R	A	P	■	T	A	B	L	E	A	U
A	■	O	■	O	■	S	■	Y	■	A	■	D
R	E	P	A	S	T	■	P	S	Y	C	H	E
S	■	S	■	T	■	■	■	S	■	H	■	L

No. 95

A	R	A	B	I	C	■	B	■	L	■	B	■
L	■	L	■	■	A	M	I	C	A	B	L	E
M	A	B	■	■	B	■	S	■	U	■	E	■
O	■	I	T	A	L	I	C	■	N	O	A	H
S	■	N	■	■	E	■	U	■	C	■	T	■
T	O	O	T	H	■	H	I	G	H	E	S	T
■	■	■	A	■	M	■	T	■	E	■	■	■
C	O	R	N	E	A	S	■	O	S	I	E	R
■	B	■	G	■	S	■	T	■	■	S	■	E
S	E	M	I	■	K	E	E	P	E	R	■	P
■	Y	■	B	■	I	■	R	■	■	A	G	E
R	E	C	L	I	N	E	R	■	■	E	■	A
■	D	■	E	■	G	■	A	M	U	L	E	T

No. 96

D	U	F	F	■	I	L	L	F	A	T	E	D
I	■	U	■	A	■	E	■	I	■	O	■	I
S	Y	N	O	N	Y	M	■	S	C	U	B	A
T	■	G	■	N	■	M	■	H	■	R	■	M
A	M	I	G	O	■	A	V	A	R	I	C	E
S	■	■	■	U	■	S	■	N	■	S	■	T
T	A	L	E	N	T	■	E	D	I	T	O	R
E	■	A	■	C	■	S	■	C	■	■	■	I
F	I	T	M	E	N	T	■	H	A	V	O	C
U	■	E	■	M	■	R	■	I	■	E	■	A
L	A	R	G	E	■	A	P	P	A	R	E	L
L	■	A	■	N	■	N	■	S	■	V	■	L
Y	U	L	E	T	I	D	E	■	L	E	V	Y

SOLUTIONS

No. 97

P	E	A	C	H	Y			S		D	U	B
	D			I		A	W	O	K	E		R
H	U	S	T	L	E	D		N		S		O
	C			A		D		S	P	E	A	K
M	A	C	A	R	O	O	N			R		E
	T			I		N		D		V		R
B	E	A	S	T	S		B	I	C	E	P	S
R		D		Y		S		S			R	
E		V			S	P	E	C	T	R	U	M
A	B	A	S	E		A		O			D	
D		N		L		S	N	U	B	B	E	D
T		C	H	A	R	M		N			N	
H	U	E		N			S	T	A	R	T	S

No. 98

P	A	P	A		F	A	M	I	L	I	E	S
E		H		D		B		N		N		P
R	A	I	D	E	R	S		V	I	D	E	O
F		A		M		E		U		U		N
E	L	L		O		I		L	I	C	I	T
C				N	Y	L	O	N		T		A
T		R		S				E		S		N
I		E		T	U	B	E	R				E
O	T	T	E	R		A		A		E	G	O
N		R		A		R		B		L		U
I	N	E	P	T		Y	E	L	L	O	W	S
S		A		O		O		E		P		L
T	U	T	O	R	I	N	G		V	E	R	Y

No. 99

	D	I	S	S	O	L	U	T	I	O	N	
M		N		U		O		H		U		S
I		F		P	I	L	A	U		S	H	Y
S	P	O	O	R		L		M		T		N
C		R		E		E		B	A	S	E	D
H	O	M	E	M	A	D	E					I
I		S		E				W		E		C
E					I	N	S	O	M	N	I	A
V	I	G	I	L		A		N		A		T
O		U		U		T		D	U	B	A	I
U	M	A		M	I	T	R	E		L		O
S		N		E		E		R		E		N
	C	O	U	N	T	R	Y	S	I	D	E	

No. 100

	P		A		T		O		E		U	
F	I	E	S	T	A		B	A	N	A	N	A
	N		C		V		O		T		T	
S	K	Y	E		E	X	E	G	E	T	I	C
			R		R		S		R		T	
A	B	A	T	I	N	G		I	T	A	L	Y
	A		A		S		R		A		E	
A	C	R	I	D		R	E	M	I	N	D	S
	C		N		A		C		N			
H	A	R	A	N	G	U	E		M	O	P	E
	R		B		A		I		E		R	
W	A	L	L	O	P		P	U	N	D	I	T
	T		E		E		T		T		M	

No. 101

L	I	F	E	P	E	E	R		C	A	V	A
O		O		R		E		S		N		T
V	I	G	G	O		R		C	A	T	C	H
E		S		P		I		A		I		L
			C	O	M	E	S	T	I	B	L	E
A		C		R		R		T		O		T
R	E	L	A	T	E		P	E	D	D	L	E
O		I		I		G		R		Y		S
M	U	M	B	O	J	U	M	B	O			
A		B		N		N		R		O		A
T	H	E	T	A		G		A	N	G	S	T
I		R		L		H		I		R		O
C	U	S	P		H	O	R	N	B	E	A	M

No. 102

A	J	A	R		R	H	E	T	O	R	I	C
R		N		F		O		R		E		O
G	O	N	D	O	L	A		A	R	G	O	N
U		E		R		R		N		A		S
M	I	X		M		D		S	W	I	N	E
E				A	E	S	O	P		N		C
N		T		L				A		S		U
T		R		D	E	B	A	R				T
A	D	E	L	E		I		E		P	H	I
T		M		H		K		N		A		V
I	R	O	N	Y		I	N	C	E	N	S	E
V		L		D		N		Y		D		L
E	S	O	T	E	R	I	C		G	A	R	Y

No. 103

D	E	D	I	C	A	T	E		O	W	E	D
R		A		I		O		D		O		A
U	T	T	E	R		U		I	V	O	R	Y
G		A		C		P		S		D		B
			S	U	P	E	R	P	O	W	E	R
S		C		M		E		E		O		E
C	H	O	O	S	E		A	N	D	R	E	A
R		M		C		C		S		M		K
I	M	P	E	R	S	O	N	A	L			
B		O		I		S		T		A		B
B	L	U	R	B		T		I	N	N	E	R
L		N		E		L		O		T		A
E	D	D	Y		H	Y	P	N	O	S	I	S

No. 104

	M		A		P		U		R		O	
L	I	Q	U	O	R		S	W	E	R	V	E
	R		T		E		U		V		E	
L	O	C	H		V	E	R	T	E	B	R	A
			O		I		P		R		T	
H	O	A	R	S	E	N		A	B	D	U	L
	D		I		W		C		E		R	
L	O	T	T	O		T	O	U	R	N	E	Y
	M		A		S		L		A			
S	E	A	R	C	H	E	D		T	E	A	M
	T		I		U		E		I		L	
D	E	T	A	I	N		S	L	O	P	P	Y
	R		N		T		T		N		S	

No. 105

A	I	D	E		P	U	S	S	Y	C	A	T
C		I		B		N		H		A		O
C	O	N	C	O	R	D		O	A	S	I	S
I		E		O		U		R		S		S
D	E	R	E	G	U	L	A	T	I	O	N	
E				I		Y		C		C		D
N	I	P	P	E	R		C	H	U	K	K	A
T		U		W		E		A				Y
	I	N	C	O	N	V	E	N	I	E	N	T
S		D		O		I		G		X		O
T	Y	I	N	G		C	R	E	S	T	E	D
U		T		I		T		D		O		A
D	I	S	P	E	R	S	E		C	L	O	Y

No. 106

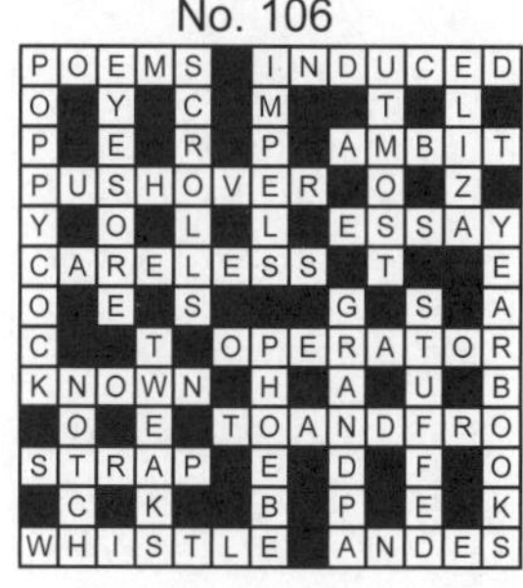

P	O	E	M	S		I	N	D	U	C	E	D
O		Y		C		M			T		L	
P		E		R		P		A	M	B	I	T
P	U	S	H	O	V	E	R		O		Z	
Y		O		L		L		E	S	S	A	Y
C	A	R	E	L	E	S	S		T			E
O		E		S				G		S		A
C			T		O	P	E	R	A	T	O	R
K	N	O	W	N		H		A		U		B
	O		E		T	O	A	N	D	F	R	O
S	T	R	A	P		E		D		F		O
	C		K			B		P		E		K
W	H	I	S	T	L	E		A	N	D	E	S

No. 107

V	E	R	S	I	O	N	S		U	T	A	H
E		E		L		I				A		E
E	M	A	I	L		B	E	G	O	N	I	A
R		G		E		B				N		D
		A		G		L	A	S	T	I	N	G
G	E	N	U	I	N	E		T		N		E
L				B				A				A
O		B		L		O	C	T	O	B	E	R
S	W	I	V	E	L	S		U		U		
S		N				C		E		N		U
A	N	A	E	M	I	A		T	A	K	E	S
R		R				R		T		U		E
Y	O	Y	O		E	S	T	E	E	M	E	D

No. 108

U	R	S	A		B	R	I	E	F	I	N	G
N		T		N		E		C		M		O
S	L	O	W	E	S	T		C	O	P	E	D
T		U		V		U		E		O		S
E	N	T	R	E	P	R	E	N	E	U	R	
A				R		N		T		N		R
D	E	P	U	T	Y		B	R	I	D	L	E
Y		R		H		S		I				C
	D	O	M	E	S	T	I	C	A	L	L	Y
A		R		L		I		I		E		C
G	L	A	D	E		N	E	T	B	A	L	L
A		T		S		T		Y		S		E
R	E	A	S	S	E	S	S		O	H	M	S

SOLUTIONS

No. 109

L	A	T	H		P	R	E	C	E	P	T	S
U		I		R		E		A		E		A
N	U	M	B	E	R	S		T	A	L	L	Y
C		E		M		I		E		I		S
H	O	R	R	O	R	S	T	R	U	C	K	
E				R		T		P		A		C
O	B	T	U	S	E		S	I	N	N	E	R
N		W		E		A		L				Y
	D	I	F	F	I	C	U	L	T	I	E	S
A		D		U		A		A		D		T
P	E	D	A	L		C	O	R	P	O	R	A
S		L		L		I		S		L		L
E	V	E	R	Y	D	A	Y		A	S	P	S

No. 110

G	A	L	E	N	A		S		T		E	
R		O			M	A	C	A	R	O	N	I
O	R	C			B		I		A		D	
T		A	P	I	E	C	E		N	A	I	L
T		T			R		N		Q		N	
O	M	E	G	A		S	C	O	U	R	G	E
			O		U		E		I			
I	S	O	L	A	T	E		B	L	E	E	P
	T		D		O		S			U		I
W	A	I	F		P	O	W	D	E	R		C
	T		I		I		E			E	L	K
M	O	U	S	S	A	K	A			K		U
	R		H		N		R	E	V	A	M	P

No. 111

S	I	M	I	A	N			Z		I	N	K
	N			S		P	L	E	A	S		E
S	T	R	I	P	E	S		T		O		S
	E			E		A		A	B	B	O	T
D	R	E	A	R	I	L	Y			A		R
	I			I		M		M		R		E
S	M	A	R	T	S		F	O	S	S	I	L
L		C		Y		A		R			N	
I		R			E	S	C	A	P	A	D	E
D	R	O	V	E		H		S			U	
I		N		L		E	S	S	E	N	C	E
N		Y	E	M	E	N		E			E	
G	E	M		S			A	S	S	I	S	I

No. 112

	F		S		A		G		S		F	
C	O	L	L	A	B	O	R	A	T	I	O	N
	U		A		A		A		U		R	
P	R	O	P	O	S	E	D		D	E	E	R
			U		H		E		I		H	
D	A	P	P	L	E	D		T	O	T	A	L
	D				D		A				N	
A	D	O	R	E		I	N	T	E	N	D	S
	I		O		A		S		X			
S	C	A	B		D	O	W	N	C	A	S	T
	T		B		I		E		E		T	
L	E	X	I	C	O	G	R	A	P	H	E	R
	D		E		S		S		T		M	

No. 113

C	H	O	I	R		C	R	A	S	H	E	S
R		X		I		A			U		R	
I		O		V		S		S	P	E	A	R
T	I	N	N	I	T	U	S		E		S	
I		I		E		A		P	R	I	E	D
Q	U	A	R	R	E	L	S		B			R
U		N		A				S		N		A
E			P		P	L	A	T	F	O	R	M
S	T	E	R	N		E		E		S		A
	H		E		S	E	A	T	B	E	L	T
A	I	S	L	E		W		S		B		I
	G		I			A		O		A		S
C	H	I	M	N	E	Y		N	I	G	H	T

No. 114

E	M	I	R		E	S	T	I	M	A	T	E
S		D		R		E		M		I		X
T	R	I	S	E	C	T		P	A	R	K	A
A		O		A		T		O		L		G
B	U	M	P	S		L	E	V	Y	I	N	G
L				S		E		E		F		E
I	N	C	H	E	S		G	R	A	T	E	R
S		L		S		S		I				A
H	E	A	D	S	E	T		S	T	U	N	T
M		R		M		A		H		N		E
E	X	I	L	E		L	E	E	W	A	R	D
N		O		N		E		D		R		L
T	I	N	C	T	U	R	E		E	M	M	Y

SOLUTIONS

No. 115

A	L	E	C		U	N	R	A	V	E	L	S
C		R		S		A		S		M		T
C	O	R	S	E	T	S		T	E	P	E	E
O		O		L		S		R		L		A
M	A	R		F		A		O	V	O	I	D
M				E	Q	U	I	P		Y		F
O		P		M				H		S		A
D		A		P	R	I	V	Y				S
A	N	N	U	L		N		S		C	A	T
T		A		O		D		I		L		N
I	T	C	H	Y		I	N	C	L	I	N	E
N		E		E		G		S		C		S
G	R	A	N	D	S	O	N		E	K	E	S

No. 116

	I		R		A		P		S		S	
I	N	S	U	B	S	T	A	N	T	I	A	L
	F		L		S		C		E		M	
C	O	V	E	N	A	N	T		E	V	E	N
			R		I		S		P		N	
F	I	R	S	T	L	Y		A	S	P	E	N
	N				S		G				S	
A	C	R	E	S		B	O	O	R	I	S	H
	U		M		A		D		O			
G	R	A	B		P	O	L	K	A	D	O	T
	R		L		P		I		S		W	
T	E	L	E	M	A	R	K	E	T	I	N	G
	D		M		L		E		S		S	

No. 117

D	E	C	A	N	T	E	R		I	S	L	E
U		R		O		R				C		T
C	H	A	S	M		M	C	E	N	R	O	E
K		V		I		I				I		R
		A		N		N	E	W	S	M	E	N
O	A	T	C	A	K	E		A		P		I
B				L				T				T
S		S		L		S	K	E	T	C	H	Y
E	N	C	R	Y	P	T		R		A		
R		O				A		P		R		S
V	E	N	D	O	R	S		O	P	E	R	A
E		E				I		L		E		N
R	A	S	H		O	S	B	O	U	R	N	E

No. 118

	F		A		S		A		P		A	
B	A	M	B	O	O		G	A	R	A	G	E
	T		B		L		I		E		I	
T	S	A	R		V	A	L	I	D	A	T	E
			E		E		E		O		A	
C	O	N	V	E	N	E		S	M	I	T	E
	P		I		T		P		I		E	
K	E	B	A	B		T	O	R	N	A	D	O
	R		T		E		P		A			
P	E	R	I	O	D	I	C		N	U	N	S
	T		O		G		O		T		A	
S	T	A	N	Z	A		R	E	L	I	V	E
	A		S		R		N		Y		E	

No. 119

L	E	P	T	O	N		F	A	B	R	I	C
I		O		R		S		Z		O		A
C	A	R	I	B	O	U		A		B		N
H		T		I		S	I	L	V	E	R	Y
E	R	U	P	T		C		E				O
N		G				E		A	P	R	O	N
		A		M	O	P	E	S		E		
P	O	L	K	A		T				T		F
A				Z		I		P	E	A	C	E
D	I	S	T	U	R	B		E		I		N
D		A		R		L	A	C	O	N	I	C
L		N		K		E		K		E		E
E	N	D	E	A	R		U	S	U	R	E	R

No. 120

S	O	L	E	M	N	L	Y		A	G	E	S
A		O		A		I				L		U
P	R	O	N	G		N	O	X	I	O	U	S
S		S		N		T				S		P
		E		I		E	N	M	A	S	S	E
B	A	S	H	F	U	L		E		Y		N
I				I				R				D
R		R		E		D	O	C	T	O	R	S
D	R	E	S	S	E	R		U		C		
B		C				O		R		E		I
A	V	O	C	A	D	O		I	D	L	E	S
T		I				P		A		O		I
H	A	L	F		I	S	O	L	A	T	E	S

SOLUTIONS

No. 121

M	A	N	D	O	L	I	N		P	O	M	P
E		E		U		B				S		E
E	X	U	L	T		E	L	I	S	I	O	N
D		T		E		R				E		I
		E		R		I	N	H	E	R	I	T
M	A	R	I	M	B	A		I		S		E
I				O				T				N
S		D		S		C	R	O	C	H	E	T
C	H	A	T	T	E	L		R		A		
H		M				U		M		W		W
I	N	S	P	E	C	T		I	D	A	H	O
E		E				C		S		I		R
F	O	L	K		T	H	E	S	P	I	A	N

No. 122

P	A	C	E	S		P	E	N	C	I	L	S
H		O		T		U			L		O	
I		N		R		R		D	O	U	S	E
L	A	C	R	O	S	S	E		T		E	
O		A		L		U		T	H	E	R	M
L	E	V	E	L	L	E	D		E			A
O		E		S				G		S		K
G			U		C	H	E	R	O	K	E	E
Y	O	U	N	G		A		A		I		S
	L		D		E	M	I	N	E	N	C	E
S	I	L	O	S		I		U		N		N
	V		N			L		L		E		S
B	E	J	E	W	E	L		E	D	D	I	E

No. 123

A	C	C	E	D	E		A		S		A	
Z		R			S	A	N	C	T	I	F	Y
A	L	I			T		O		Y		F	
L		S	E	L	E	C	T		L	E	A	K
E		I			R		H		I		I	
A	S	S	E	T		G	E	Y	S	E	R	S
			M		B		R		T			
S	C	H	E	M	E	D		A	S	I	D	E
	I		R		A		P			N		N
B	R	I	G		T	I	L	T	E	D		M
	C		I		R		O			U	R	E
Q	U	A	N	T	I	F	Y			C		S
	S		G		X		S	C	O	T	C	H

No. 124

	N		S		S		C		R		S	
C	I	R	C	U	M	F	E	R	E	N	C	E
	R		A		I		D		M		I	
P	O	R	R	I	D	G	E		A	I	M	S
			C		G		D		R		I	
L	O	W	E	R	E	D		S	K	A	T	E
	V				N		F				A	
M	E	L	T	S		E	A	R	M	A	R	K
	R		Y		H		R		I			
F	L	A	P		A	D	M	O	N	I	S	H
	O		I		N		E		U		H	
C	O	N	F	I	G	U	R	A	T	I	O	N
	K		Y		S		S		E		W	

No. 125

J	E	A	L	O	U	S	Y		O	R	C	A
O		L		V		E		A		E		V
S	T	A	L	E		R		M	A	C	H	O
H		S		R		A		B		E		I
			S	I	M	P	L	I	F	I	E	D
S		R		N		H		D		V		I
Y	I	E	L	D	S		H	E	R	E	I	N
N		A		U		A		X		D		G
D	E	C	E	L	E	R	A	T	E			
R		T		G		T		R		S		L
O	P	I	N	E		H		O	U	T	D	O
M		V		D		U		U		A		T
E	W	E	R		P	R	E	S	A	G	E	S

No. 126

E	R	A	S		A	P	P	R	O	A	C	H
N		D		L		O		E		C		I
T	I	M	P	A	N	I		F	E	T	I	D
H		I		B		S		R		U		E
A	S	T	R	O	N	O	M	I	C	A	L	
L				R		N		G		T		A
P	O	P	L	A	R		D	E	M	E	A	N
Y		I		T		B		R				G
	A	E	R	O	D	Y	N	A	M	I	C	S
I		R		R		E		T		D		T
R	I	C	C	I		B	R	O	I	L	E	R
I		E		E		Y		R		E		O
S	I	D	E	S	T	E	P		A	D	A	M

No. 127

	O		F		F		S		U		P	
A	R	M	O	U	R		T	A	N	N	E	D
	B		R		A		E		D		D	
A	S	H	E		Z	E	P	P	E	L	I	N
			K		Z		S		R		G	
S	W	I	N	D	L	E		U	S	U	R	Y
	A		O		E		T		T		E	
B	R	A	W	L		S	H	E	A	R	E	R
	R		L		S		E		N			
F	I	V	E	S	T	A	R		D	I	A	Z
	O		D		A		A		I		V	
C	R	A	G	G	Y		P	I	N	I	O	N
	S		E		S		Y		G		N	

No. 128

V	I	R	T	U	O	S	O		K	I	E	V
A		O		N		T				M		O
M	O	U	N	D		A	R	C	H	A	I	C
P		T		O		T				G		A
		E		U		I	N	F	L	E	C	T
A	E	R	O	B	I	C		O		S		I
N				T				R				V
S		M		E		M	A	G	N	A	T	E
W	E	E	K	D	A	Y		O		M		
E		T				S		T		B		W
R	E	E	N	A	C	T		T	O	U	C	H
E		O				I		E		S		Y
D	A	R	T		A	C	A	N	T	H	U	S

No. 129

P	A	T	H		O	C	C	U	P	I	E	D
R		A		Q		H		N		M		E
I	N	C	L	U	D	E		R	O	P	E	S
M		I		I		R		E		E		T
E	A	T		N		U		A	L	D	E	R
M				T	U	B	E	S		E		U
I		I		E				O		D		C
N		K		S	P	A	W	N				T
I	T	E	M	S		R		A		P	S	I
S		B		E		D		B		A		V
T	W	A	I	N		E	L	L	I	P	S	E
E		N		C		N		E		E		L
R	E	A	G	E	N	T	S		T	R	A	Y

No. 130

A	N	T	E	C	E	D	E		M	E	N	U
P		A		O		A		S		P		N
E	Q	U	A	L		N		H	O	I	S	T
X		T		L		U		A		D		E
			H	A	M	B	U	R	G	E	R	S
P		I		B		E		P		M		T
R	A	N	S	O	M		A	S	P	I	R	E
E		S		R		S		H		C		D
A	T	T	R	A	C	T	I	O	N			
M		A		T		A		O		A		E
B	I	N	G	O		N		T	E	P	I	D
L		C		R		C		E		E		G
E	Y	E	S		B	E	G	R	U	D	G	E

No. 131

I	D	L	E		R	E	P	U	B	L	I	C
N		A		B		A		N		E		H
S	A	N	D	A	L	S		D	R	A	M	A
I		C		T		I		E		K		R
G	R	E	A	T		N	I	R	V	A	N	A
N				L		G		A		G		C
I	N	S	T	E	P		A	C	C	E	P	T
F		E		G		T		H				E
I	N	S	U	R	E	R		I	N	C	U	R
C		S		O		O		E		A		L
A	D	I	E	U		I	N	V	O	L	V	E
N		O		N		K		E		L		S
T	O	N	E	D	E	A	F		U	S	E	S

No. 132

B	R	U	S	H		B	E	H	A	V	E	D
E		T		E		R			T		X	
E		T		A		O		C	R	A	I	G
K	N	E	A	D	I	N	G		I		S	
E		R		M		Z		M	U	F	T	I
E	L	E	V	A	T	E	D		M			N
P		D		N				M		F		D
E			B		C	A	R	A	P	A	C	E
R	I	F	L	E		L		N		C		M
	M		A		T	U	N	G	S	T	E	N
I	B	I	Z	A		M		E		U		I
	U		E			N		R		A		T
G	E	O	R	G	I	A		S	U	L	K	Y

No. 133

S	C	A	T	H	E		S	P	I	D	E	R
E		C		Y		B		R		R		W
E	C	H	I	D	N	A		O		A		A
T		I		R		C	A	V	E	M	A	N
H	Y	E	N	A		K		O				D
E		V				P		S	O	F	I	A
		E		R	O	A	S	T		O		
N	U	D	G	E		C				R		A
I				B		K		D	U	M	P	S
M	A	R	T	I	N	I		E		U		I
B		E		R		N	I	B	B	L	E	D
L		A		T		G		U		A		E
E	A	R	T	H	S		E	G	R	E	S	S

No. 134

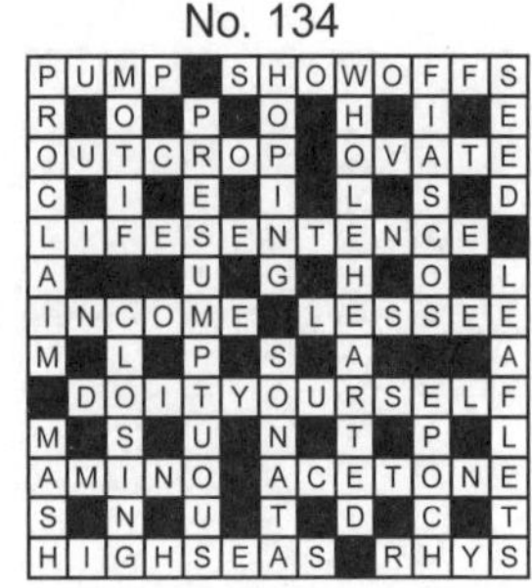

P	U	M	P		S	H	O	W	O	F	F	S
R		O		P		O		H		I		E
O	U	T	C	R	O	P		O	V	A	T	E
C		I		E		I		L		S		D
L	I	F	E	S	E	N	T	E	N	C	E	
A				U		G		H		O		L
I	N	C	O	M	E		L	E	S	S	E	E
M		L		P		S		A				A
	D	O	I	T	Y	O	U	R	S	E	L	F
M		S		U		N		T		P		L
A	M	I	N	O		A	C	E	T	O	N	E
S		N		U		T		D		C		T
H	I	G	H	S	E	A	S		R	H	Y	S